ARMISTICE 100 DAYS

ARMISTICE 100 DAYS
In memory of 100 people
from the First World War:
their stories told in 100 words
by 100 writers

26

The book of centenas by writers from 26
to mark the centenary of Armistice Day,
11 November 2018.

In partnership with Imperial War Museums.

With donations to War Child.

First published in 2018
by 26 Characters Ltd
5 Cromwell Place
London SW7 2JE

ISBN 978-1-5272-2852-8

British Library Cataloguing in Publication Data.
A catalogue record for this book is available from the British Library.

Designed by David Carroll & Co
Printed by Pureprint Group Limited
Typefaces Plantin (1913) and Johnston (1916)

1 3 5 7 9 10 8 6 4 2

CONTENTS

INTRODUCTION

Only connect. EM Forster's epigraph to *Howards End* has become my mantra for life. This Armistice project absolutely demonstrates its spirit.

A couple of years ago someone I knew as a colleague at Interbrand and then as a client at BP recommended a writer to me. David Bickerton put me in touch with Lisa Andrews, and we met for a coffee. Much of my life seems to revolve around meeting people for a coffee. I liked Lisa and saw that she had great qualities both as a writer and an organiser. She co-edited her own website, allthesins.co.uk, that takes an idiosyncratic look at cultural issues and helps other writers and artists find a creative outlet for their work, and she was interested in writing projects that would develop and stretch her – into new areas both of business and creative writing.

That's a good and, in many ways, typical profile for members of the writing group 26 that I had co-founded in 2003. Since then we have carried off a wide variety of writing projects with our members, partnering with national organisations such as the V&A, British Library and National Museum of Scotland.

Lisa joined 26. In the meantime, I had begun writing a new novel called *The Good Messenger* that is set either side of the First World War and, for its central section, on Armistice Day 1918, seen through the eyes of a young woman at that time. That novel had been scheduled for publication near Armistice Day 2018.

When Lisa and I met next we were more consciously exploring opportunities for a 26 creative project. Our discussion centred on the First World War and the approaching centenary of Armistice. Lisa knew a person who might help bring about a meeting with Imperial War Museums. She took the initiative and sent an email to IWM to introduce 26 and suggest that we might have an interesting conversation about a project.

So we did. In August 2017 Lisa and I met Liz Robertson and Pamela Linden and talked about IWM's Armistice centenary plans and how 26 might fit into them. Bowled over by their enthusiasm, we raised our ambitions too. Instead of a conventional 26 project involving just 26 writers we suggested that we would recruit 100 writers. I then proposed a new literary form for this special project: the centena, exactly 100 words, with the opening three words repeated as the final three, providing an intriguing opening and a satisfying close.

Many more meetings and discussions took place before we were ready to invite 100 writers to sign up. We didn't need to hold our breaths; 100 writers volunteered almost instantly from our membership. They included Lisa Andrews (of course) and David Bickerton, our original connection; plus well-known poets such as Michael Longley and Jacob Sam-La Rose; novelists such as Miranda Dickinson and Elise Valmorbida;

and writers from companies such as McLaren and Hitachi. Wonderful diversity – and we were pleased, too, that the writers, reflecting the global nature of our subject, were from all parts of the world: UK, Ireland, Australia, New Zealand, the Caribbean, Canada, USA, South Africa, India as well as several writers in different countries of Europe (including Germany).

Each was asked to choose a subject: a person alive at the time of the First World War. We encouraged writers to think beyond the obvious combatants in the front-line trenches. What about the women, the conscientious objectors, those from the less documented areas of life and society at the time? When the writers came back with their suggestions we were delighted by the diversity. We set in place an editorial system so that eleven volunteer editors could liaise with individual writers to make the centenas the best they could be.

IWM provided links to organisations that were their 'centenary partners' – museums, archives and cultural institutions nationally and internationally, as well as their own digital resource *Lives of the First World War*. The latter was particularly useful for those, including myself, who were investigating family history. Interesting creative journeys unfolded, and we asked each writer to record these in fewer than 500 words for the IWM website.

Then the centenas were written, edited and posted daily from 5th August with the creation story to back them up. We had applied for but failed to receive Heritage Lottery Fund money to produce a book of the centenas. As a not-for-profit organisation with limited funds this gave 26 a problem. But now, as we read the extraordinary range and quality of the work, it seemed clear that we had a responsibility to publish the complete collection of centenas in book form. The people written about, whose lives had inspired us and connected us as writers to that period of history, deserved a memorial in printed form.

So, we decided to publish the book as a 26 book, not to make money but to honour the memories of the people whose lives and deaths had touched us deeply. We agreed that there should be a charity link, with profits (after production costs were covered) going to War Child to help children damaged by war.

Now you are holding that book in your hands. We raised the money and produced the book, thanks to the efforts of people mentioned by Lisa Andrews in the Acknowledgements. It has been an amazing project, one in which all involved can take great pride.

Now please read the centenas – they will move you, stir you, sometimes bring you to tears. That is the power of words and the power of human beings to inspire words. *Only connect.*

John Simmons
One of 26's founding directors

FOREWORD

In January 2018, the IWM First World War
Centenary Partnership team and the 26
committee met in the former reading room
beneath the famous dome of the Imperial War
Museum. It was an appropriate location to agree
our project to mark the close of the centenary
of the First World War. We would work together
to ask 100 writers to write 100 works of 100
words, to tell the story of 100 individuals who
experienced the First World War; and we would
release one each day over the last 100 days of
the centenary of the conflict on the IWM's
centenary social media channels, and use this
to highlight the commemoration activity of
100 members of the Centenary Partnership.
Over the coming months, web pages were
commissioned, study visits for writers organised,
and dozens of research queries answered, whilst
26 commissioned and edited the works, and July
was spent uploading the centenas and devising
the campaign. A real team effort.

Almost every place and every family has a
First World War story, and IWM's First World
War Centenary Partnership has supported the
thousands of organisations across the world to
tell their stories of the conflict. It was the first
conflict to be extensively recorded - on film,
in photographs, through letters and diaries,
reported in newspapers, and captured in official

records. Those records have inspired these works, and the writers have given a voice to characters enclosed in museums, archives and family history. Listen to the voices: they will move and inspire, and ensure the experiences of millions of ordinary men and women of the First World War are not forgotten.

Katie Childs
IWM First World War Centenary Partnership

ACKNOWLEDGEMENTS

We are all connected by stories. They are woven into the very fabric of our humanity – they teach us, warn us, inspire us and even, sometimes, reflect what is good in us. Some are handed down through families, others are universal, passed along community lines. Still others reveal hidden gems that might otherwise have been lost under dust-flecked layers of time.

The pages of this wonderful book are filled with such stories and connections. What's more, each of our 100 writers is now inextricably linked by their mutual desire to honour the men, women and children whose lives were so altered by four years of total war. It is safe to say that the people who inspired these centenas have left an indelible mark on us and, as you read each one, I hope that they will whisper something of themselves to you, too.

What our writers have achieved in this project is extraordinary, and thanks, first and foremost, must go to them – we would have no book without such beautiful work.

Thanks, too, to everyone who helped us raise the funds, so that we might create a permanent memorial to our centena subjects and help support War Child's vital work.

But a project of this scale requires many pairs of hands and I would also like to thank:

John Simmons – for asking me to help bring his idea to life and for pushing me – always kindly, always supportively – to make my own writing better.

Becca Magnus – for her beautifully-designed digital centenas, as well as her invaluable role on the project and editorial teams.

Neil Baker and *Ed Prichard* – for being wonderful project team members and editors.

Sue Evans – for her wise counsel as both my editor and the project team's guide throughout the book's production process.

Our other amazing editors, *Lucy Beevor, Rishi Dastidar, Wendy Jones, Elen Lewis* and *Richard Pelletier* – for putting up with my never-ending requests.

David Carroll – for designing the beautiful book you now hold in your hands.

Rachel Marshall – for posting all 100 centenas on 26's website.

Michelle Nicol – for helping us spread the word on social media.

Bridget Waters – for her invaluable fundraising advice.

26 chairman *Martin Clarkson* – for sending the project team notes that said 'this book will happen'.

Mark Woods and *Phil Richardson* of *Pureprint* – for helping us get this book printed.

G . F Smith – for the company's generous support supplying paper for this book.

Pamela Linden, Liz Robertson, Katie Childs and *Bethany Reynard* from Imperial War Museums' First World War Partnership – for their passion, belief and support for this project right from the very first meeting.

Finally, to each of the subjects who inspired this remarkable body of work, many of whom have shown me that it is compassion in the face of horror that echoes loudest through history.

Lest we forget.

Lisa Andrews

THE MEMORIAL LIST

THE CENTENAS

001 – 100

ANGUS GRUNDY

The Chauffeur's Turn

'War was inevitable—
"powder keg", wasn't it?

I'd served empire, risked my neck,
won Count Harrach's favour.

Summoned for manoeuvres,
he goes, "We'll drive!"

From *Vienna*?
An eighteen-day slog!

In Sarajevo,
the Archduke fancies
our Gräf & Stift—lid down,
sunshine, crowds—
wife on display.

That *first* grenade?
My wits saved us.
Detonates under
Merrizzi's motorcar.

Ferdinand's livid:
"Welcomed with bombs!
Scandalous!"

Off to hospital, visit Merrizzi.
Detour—
Only, I'm not told, see?

"Wrong turn!"
Fine, I reverse.

Princip's waiting
wild-eyed –
shoots twice,
point blank.
Him. Her.
No hope.

Crawling with assassins, turns out.

– Another pint?
No, war was inevitable…'

Inspired by Leopold Lojka

THERESE KIERAN

Stitches in Time

A needle's eye threw her a lifeline:
between finger & thumb
she pinched silver to make a little gold,
told her story via business card:

> JEANNE DE-NEVE & SISTERS
> Belgian Embroiders, (late of Maline)

to Ireland's muddy hem, she trailed a running
    stitch:
each stitch a step from Mechelen to Monaghan
each stitch a suture mending hearts of women,
    of men.

She knew the good of soft tarantulle on skin
trained local women,
helped Bel-Broid spread its wings,

clung to kith & kin:
refugees, she never knew they'd be,
their French knots undone, in history-making
steely, through a needle's eye.

Inspired by Jeanne De-Neve

MIRANDA DICKINSON

Waiting in Watson's Portrait Studio, Leeds

I wait, alone.

The lilies in my hand tremble, but the studio is still.

I've hidden your letter in my shoe, for luck. The one with your sketch of the dress I now wear. Forty-eight hours' leave was long enough to make me Mrs Ellis, but not our photograph.

'Ready now,' Mr Watson says, holding the flash. His son is fighting in France, too.

I'm scared, Fred. But I smile my brightest for both of us.

I will carry our dreams while you are gone. Always your bride, forever your Evelyn. Praying you home.

Please come home.

I wait, alone.

Inspired by Gertrude Evelyn Ellis

JACOB SAM-LA ROSE

The King Said All Englishmen Must Go To Join The War

On a frontline, Gershom
and Eustace, deep in labrish
and banter of back home,
whatever they've staked
against being here, exactly
where they want to be, down
to the blood and bone, beneath
the skin, wherever the hooks of
king and empire root and tug
most deeply, *glad to go*, regardless
how unwanted, regardless of their
early fervour, Gershom still a teen
    – all this, before Eustace meets
a shell, becomes another unmarked death
regardless of the skin he wears
and Gershom lives
to see the century out, and reminisce
on how it was to be a soldier,
on a frontline.

Inspired by Gershom Browne

EZRI CARLEBACH

To resist war

To resist war requires more than the avoidance of trenches. It demands trenchancy, such as few can possess. Among them stands Karl Kraus, iconoclast of language, herald of *The Last Days of Mankind*.

Poet, playwright, publisher, performer, polemicist, Shakespearian scholar, reciter, and translator, arch-critic of corruption among Vienna's venerated stage and *feuilletonist* page, the anti-journalist, scorned and adulated, a mind even Freud feared; Kraus lit the torch to light the way to truth.

While Europe yielded to Jingo's call Kraus remained resolute against it. Armed only with *Die Fackel* (lit. 'the torch'), the Apocalyptic Satirist enlisted words to resist war.

Inspired by Karl Kraus

ED PRICHARD

Catching the train from Abertridwr to Gallipoli, 1952

Dardanelles-denelles-denelles

he never come home

no

died of wounds

ei clwyfau goch★

in the Dardanelles

they said

sounds like a train

I'll find him fetch him in the train
he'll be pleased the dog we've ham for the
journey for the jour

dog ham train

pleased

is the Dardanelles like Abertridwr?

up and over rolling green and Chapel black beneath

out of the mines fresh air
sea air

good for him

they say my mind's unbuckled

nonsense

my girls, my poor girls

he died but you served

enough now enough

hurry Catherine hurry

get you to the

Dardanelles-denelles-denelles

he never

Inspired by Catherine Saunders
*Welsh: 'his wounds red'

LUCY FURLONG

Votes For Women

Once a Militant, always a Militant
until the Vote was won. 'Look Here'
I said 'You may have talked Mrs Fawcett over, but
don't try those tricks on us, please. We shall
see through the whole thing too clearly.'
The Suffragettes were like eels.
Prison! It was not prison for me.
Hunger strikes! They had no fears for me.
Cat and Mouse net! I could have laughed.
'The Militants, when their prisoners are released,
will fight for their country
as they have fought for the Vote.'
Women were Voters. My Suffragette
pilgrimage was ended. But
I was once a Militant.

Inspired by Annie Kenney

SOPHIE OLSZOWSKI

Conscience or Cowardice?

A white feather floated from the gallery as the
judge sent you down.

'Too young, at eighteen, to have a conscience'
he scorned. 'When you grow up you'll know it's
right to fight.'

Stitching mailbags in prison light left you
struggling, for sight, then for work: 'Who wants
a conchie teacher?' they asked, scared you'd
subvert their children with absurd ideas: beat
swords into ploughshares, spears into pruning
hooks. They said it was the war to end them all.
But they lied, as still they lie. As now do you.
At peace. Clutching, as if at straws, a white
feather.

Inspired by Harold Bing

DOUGLAS HOWATT

One Woman Quietly Changes the World

Quietly, hopefully waiting, she read the wooden door's markings: *Marine Recruiting Command.* When would the door open? A line of whispering women waited behind her. The typewritten form fluttered in her hand. She turned to her watch. To the door. And behind her. She felt the air move before anyone else. 'Come in, ladies!' cried the man at the door. She stepped into the draft, sweeping the women behind her and their heirs ahead in a hurricane of change. The world of men now the world of people.

Today, she again faces wood – unmarked despite her successors – quietly, hopefully waiting.

Inspired by US Marine Sergeant Opha May Johnson

KARTIK KOMPELLA

Belief Betrayed

'I don't understand!'

'Citizens *need* to be loyal to their government.'

'But spilling *our* soldiers' blood for *their* war?
Rather we should plunge our knives into the
British when they are down.'

'We need not conduct ourselves poorly with the
government over the atrocities committed by
certain individuals. Let our graciousness inspire
them into giving us our freedom. The high
ground is available to both.'

Four years later...

'Some gratitude, they're working on laws to
throw our people in jail!'

'Disappointing. We will fight for our
independence.'

'Shall I recruit soldiers?'

'No, our war will be non-violent'

'I don't understand!'

Inspired by Mahatma Gandhi

JOHN SIMMONS

Jessie, Jessie and Ce

Harry looked up
as a cloud crossed the sun,
casting shadows
over the letter he was writing to me,
Jessie, and the girls, Jessie and Ce.

Bet he was listening to
the birds,
the birds, he always loved them
singing.

'Earth's same here as anywhere,'
he's writing
as the birds sang
as the cloud crossed
as the plane roared.

But he wasn't listening for
the plane,
the plane but he'd not heard it
screaming.

So me and the girls
never got the letter he was writing,
only the bullets sounding,
the last thing he was thinking
as Harry looked up.

Inspired by Jessie Branch

STUART DELVES

Last ship home

Saw.
Cross.
Water.
The saw for amputation. The nailed Christ to steady
the hand. The water to ease sweating brows. Amidst
the blackened earth and corporeal mayhem, fall
out from a war tossed hither and thither on the
horns of hubris, Elsie Inglis – small in stature,
unstoppable in will – took succour to thousands
with her army of women with tender hands. At
the end, nursing cancer's hidden scythe, she
whispered: 'I am going over to the other
side.' We can only pray, for the fallen,
that it was ineffable healing in the
visage of love that she saw
'cross water.

Inspired by Dr Elsie Inglis

GILLIAN COLHOUN

I Know You By Your Name

Black
ink stains
fracture the dove grey
clouds.

The savage sky leans over and spits out
seventeen bombs
Crazed with the bloodlust of a shark's
sixth sense
They blindly crash into quiet; rupturing
taut canvas and human flesh.

Annie, a Derry girl, builds a wall
around her hoping heart
Holds her nerve, holds her friend, holds
her patients' lives
Nurses them in threads of white cotton
and crimson cross.

Fibres rewoven into love and something
more than love
A blanket, softly shielding, calling
surrender to suffering
Soaking up enough tears to wash clean
every one of those

Black ink stains.

Inspired by Nurse Annie Rebecca Colhoun

MAIA SWIFT

The Rounds

Knock knock.

War is here, inside this satchel.

On the garden path.

Behind curtains that twitch and a door that waits.

In unsteady hands.

Soil and sweat and terror, released like gas,
spread to carpet and coasters and tea.

Cold rain creeps up primrose walls.

A sigh, unfolded in the crinkle of paper, drowns
out the birds.

A kiss, indented in ink, brings the one who isn't
here, here, to the chair, by the fire.

Boots in the hall, just for a minute.

Is it good news? Will there ever be again?

Promise to return.

Now, onwards.

Knock knock. War.

Inspired by Violet Jackson

CHARLOTTE MACKENZIE

Change some plates

On the road to Ypres,
We've passed poor remnants of humanity
  alongside little wooden crosses.
Still, I am pleased that a woman
  should get such a chance.
With Daddy Blow at the wheel, we are such
  a long way from home, Mrs Norman and I.
The girls all look so smart in their uniform,
  their efforts backing up the boys.
Along the way, the comforting smell of
  bacon reminds me of home.
Cartridges, grenades and bombs of every kind,
  all strewn upon the ground.
It's not easy getting a large camera
  down into the mud.
I must change some plates.

Inspired by Olive Edis

OLLY DAVY

Für das Vaterland*

Für das Vaterland
The Hauptmann grips the table
Fingers bleached by rage
Lusting for the Mauser's heft.
Rough wool chafes
Tributaries of sweat
As my greatcoat thaws.
It's 5am, again.
Six kilometres from sleep,
Seven metres beneath the sludge
Where my school friends died.
In this warm and cosy hell
Discovered by lamplight
Dancing from decanter
To wash basin
I've endured the vengeance
Of a monster
Since before the frost.
Breath snatched
From air whipped thick
By the Hauptmann's poison tongue.
For two hours
With back parade-ground straight,
And feet cramping in new boots,
I pray
Für das Vaterland

Inspired by Wilhelm zur Linden
German: For the Fatherland

HESTER THOMAS

Thomas Whitehead

Nothing was said. About you being a
conscientious objector (CO).

Arrested in 1916 and court-martialled, you were
sent on an alternative Cook's Tour: Pontefract
Barracks, Ferriby, Withernsea plus Wormwood
Scrubs, Wakefield and Dartmoor prisons. Hard
labour meant you spent your first month in
solitary confinement working on coarse mailbags.
And no visitors, letters or reading matter.

An artist to the core, you left a saucy pencil
sketch – a semi-nude young woman – in Peter
Carton's (CO) autograph book, then used
charcoal and chalk on brown parcel paper to
portray Charles Humphries (CO).

You left your mark but. Nothing was said.

Inspired by Tom Whitehead

ANN GORECKI

Unsung hero

Before her time.
Her ideas had travelled from the future.
What we accept as life, was ahead of her world.

Advocate of a healthy life;
Trouser-adopting and corset-abandoning.
Unsung, hardly known, history out-written.

Independent in thoughts and actions;
    sidestepping seemliness.
Volunteering, organising others as 'sisters' in Cairo.
Cooking, caring, noticing the lurking and unseen
    enemy.

Brave, becoming an agent to prevent and treat
    infection.
Saving lives with Cody's crystals, condoms and
    calomel
Whilst others preached abstinence with stopped
    ears and blindfolded eyes.

Ettie Rout. Hero and pariah.

Died at a time of her choosing but, for others,
Before her time.

Inspired by Ettie Rout

TONY CLARKE

Richardson's Recruits

'Two years lost,' laments Lt. Colonel Edwin
Heautenville Richardson. Two years of countless
'runners', upright, slow-moving targets, snagged
on barbed wire, gassed, shot, their vital messages
– 'advance', 'retreat', 'send reinforcements' –
delayed or undelivered. Perhaps it was ahead of
its time, this conviction he had, that 'four legs
good, two legs bad.' Now the penny has finally
dropped for the top brass, and his new recruits
sit to attention on the Shoeburyness grass, ears
pricked to the brutal symphony of the heavy guns
across the sea, a new breed of runners-to-be. But
who bears the cost of those two years lost?

Inspired by Edwin Heautenville Richardson

GILLIAN MCKEE

Let Him Go

'Let him go.' A sister's plea to father for her
brother's honour quest. To right the wrongs, to
curb the threat, to stand in unity. To heroes be,
we bright young things clamoured for a glamour
built on false ideals.

Too late we thought to question more, to ask,
to probe, the whys and wherefores of this war.
Loved ones leave and don't return. Unscathed
by battle, I am scarred by war.

My hands nurse men broken in body, mind and
soul. My heart mourns for him and them and a
lost generation. I live on and let him go.

Inspired by Vera Brittain

RISHI DASTIDAR

a mile a half of fire

he goes again
the message cannot wait

a duplicate to Epéhy
too much riot, smoke for another way

thrice his mount shot, undone
tremble over he waits, runs

his privilege to crawl, play dead
lie exhausted, carry on

forth, back, forth, a sowar
across a mile a half of fire

across a mile a half of fire
forth, back, forth, a sowar

lies exhausted, carries on
his privilege to crawl, play dead

tremble over he waits, runs
thrice his mount shot, undone

too much riot, smoke for another way
a duplicate to Epéhy

the message cannot wait
he goes again

Inspired by Lance-Daffadar Gobind Singh

LISA ALLEN

148

Her eighth child was low in the family ranking.
English hearts had warmed to Mr Schmitt's
streusels, but war dismantles loyalty. Amy's
eighth sailed 9000 miles to be known as Smith.

She knew nothing of travel. How, then, to
comprehend that he had retraced 8852 of those
miles to fall on the Menin Road, killed by his
countrymen? One of many, as at home: the
earth-worker swallowed by the mud.

She is also one of many – silent, ravaged
mothers. Political freedom draws near, but he
is gone, and she wants to tell him he was always
noticed, her eighth child.

Inspired by Amy Schmitt and her son George

MARGARET WEBSTER

Mrs Amy Beechey,
10th April 1918

'Give them willingly', I instructed myself on the
train to London to meet the King and Queen.

'Give your curtsy, your smile, your respect.'

But, as I waited in line to be received, my mind
filled with visions of my sweet beautiful sons –
Barnard, Frank, Harold, Charles, Leonard.

All consumed in their ravenous trenches.

I saw the bland haughty face of the King.

And I heard the condescending comfort of the
Queen – 'Thank you, Mrs Beechey, for your
great sacrifice.'

So, I told her right to her Royal face – 'It was no
sacrifice, Ma'am. I did not give them willingly.'

Inspired by Mrs Amy Beechey

LISA ANDREWS

In service of humanity

says his name is sumner and that life is sacred
but tell that to the fishes and the higher-ups
since this husk is a tatter of nerves and a glister
    of scars

says his name and it is a bugle-bright call to arms
that I cannot answer with his too-fresh skin
and his old-as-Methuselah eyes

says his name and it sounds like summer
and for a moment the stink of blistering flesh is
    swept away
by the sweet tang of newly-mown grass

it is a smell worth fighting for
but the question is am I?

so I says his name.

Inspired by Horace Reginald Sumner

REBECCA DOWMAN

Sister-in-arms

My kid brother, locked in a guardroom.

Barely 21; he should be in college now, learning
to live. (As should I, but this hateful war
degrades wisdom too.)

In our 30 minutes we criss-cross the barracks'
yard. I share friends' advice on his court martial
that the censors would erase. Before the iron
brute of the law, he is light-starved pale but calm
and firm as a rock.

I schooled him in climbing trees, now he teaches
me. Let authority do its worst; the fine few do
have power.

I'll challenge convention as never before; because
of him, my kid brother.

Inspired by Leila and Philip Taliesin Davies

ROBIN HARRIES

A Good War

A good war. One mile high in a canvas kite.
Wood and glue. Noise. Screaming wind. Oil
smoke.

No parachute. Wings that snap back and fold
off. You could. Freeze. Or faint. Or be shot or
burned or crushed. Or fall. Lots to think on,
cold hands sweating and teeth chattering, pallid
and wide eyed.

A good war. The Marne. Loos. A squadron.
The Somme. The Piave. Acclaim. Decorations.
Promotion.

Then the philandering. Disgrace. A public
divorce. Estrangement and emigration. And a
headstone on the far side of the world with a
spelling mistake.

But all same. A good war.

Inspired by Reginald Mills

RONNIE MACKINTOSH

He Came Back

In those flames he lives it again
and again. The kindled pine's lick
and spit and crack take him back,
to the charges at Marne and Aisne,
the shouts, the screams. To the
bodies torn after Ypres blasts. To
Pozieres and Passchendaele. Over
and over, that hell, in fields of mud,
layered with mucky blood, littered
with the dead and dying.

With barely buried sadness she
watches her boy, whisky in hand,
cold, old eyes fixed on a hearth that
provides no comfort. She thanks God
he came back, and for never knowing
the horrors that lurk in those flames.

Inspired by John Mackintosh

SAMUEL CROSBY

'One, another'

His beckoning caw, distant and cold
The scratch of a boot echoes deep in the well of it
Flocks sear a line in the burning white sky of it
Mud-musk and metal-tangs bleed on its edge
A youngster, unshaven and writhing, dies
Tracing folds in the face of his sweetheart

In the last, just a droplet
Ripple to join the immeasurable whole

Great rolling swells pay their loads to far shores
Allowing the other

Away from the poison and fug of the trench
The nimble savage abroad
Face to the trial
Golden in spite of it
Answers his beckoning caw

Inspired by Duke Paoa Kahanamoku

JAYNE WORKMAN

WRITE HOME FIRST.

Miss M. Wilson.
She's the soft Scottish lilt on her mother's lips,
The youngest of six, New Zealanders now,
A sister to shearers, Arthur and Jim,
Mack's promise of love on the other side.
She's the unseen wave from a Wellington quay,
A confusion of places, feeling between,
Dominion's duty to a home yet unseen,
The tailor of suits that no one will wear.
She's the pinning of hopes like a badge to lapels,
Loss measured out, with nothing to spare.
She's the name on an envelope sent 12,000 miles,
The needle of grief, threaded over again.
Miss M. Wilson.

Inspired by Margaret Wilson

NICKI LETTS

My Country

They will be proud of this.
Boys come over here,
you're wanted – they said.
An adventure too grand to miss.
(A few bucks too.)

Quick name switch, now I am equal. Lying
in sludge flipping coins in the sickly smell of
m'half-buried mates and rum. Red dust and
flies. Air hot bright thick as Mundrabilla. We wait
for the Sun Mother to paint the sky red to black,
then stumble'n'fall in pitch darkness, stragglers
for the drover. No *coo-ee!* between enemies. We
die together, whitefella and me. The king's praise
a forgotten dream. But My Country – proud
they will be.

Inspired by Private Gordon Charles Naley

NEIL BAKER

Those Shot at Dawn

We hear you Jesse
in the mutinous dark
telling the boys on the bridge
to let the lads pass
so the already dead
can live a last night.

We hear you Jesse
begging the Court Martial
sorry for what you'd said
a drop too much to drink
the spotless service
your wife and two girls.

We hear you Jesse
bound to the stake
sober with the fear
sack-mouthed whispering
for Dinah
as your mates take drunken aim
at your handkerchief heart
and fire.

There is no crown of death
or mask of shame
don't play their game.

We hear you.

Inspired by Corporal Jesse Robert Short

CAROL MCKAY

Front Line

She can't know, but she imagines. *Died*
of wounds. The Enemy bombarded.
She's entrenched in her widowhood.

His friend's letters shield her:
In billets in Arras. Church parade in the morning!
Not: *all day in a shell-hole, thirty yards from the enemy.*

At last, he can visit.
She knows what he tells her: unimaginable
    place names.
Monts-en-Ternais. Foufflin-Ricametz.
Not: *attacked with the bayonet.*

In bed, passion-needy, he bellows, reliving
artillery barrage opened.
Not: *Military Medal.*

He fights. She labours on her personal front line,
then writes. Will he love him, this boy, born
    from carnage?
She imagines. She can't know.

Inspired by Isabella McIntyre

BERT PREECE

Though you are of the border, I am of the woods

I'll stand up before the King.

I'll explain how we fought the ice and
the savage lice and the shrapnel and
metal that dropped night after night.

I'll tell him how Brighton is Bombay –
Gold and white.
How we prayed.
How I threw eight men from left to right.

From left to right.

Did you hear about my brother?

I lost my voice to the poison gas.
It bound us like these white sheets.
But I lost my voice for a reason:
So India can begin to find its own.

Before the King, I'll stand up.
I'll stand up.

Inspired by Mir Dast

LOU STEGGALS

Lucky Bean

My lucky bean; a trinket from an invalided
soldier grateful for 'something bright to think
about'. The encore of *Mother Machree* driving
out the echoes of gunfire from his memories.

Back home, I'm told, the Kingsway's regular
curtain call is the air raid siren.

Here, near the trenches of Rouen, there's no call,
no curtains at all – instead I glimpse dear Ivor
dressing in a dark crevice – his new *Home Fires*
are spluttering candles on a trunk.

Yet I feel somehow safe in the familiar warmth
of the rapturous audience. I smile. Because now
I have my lucky bean.

Inspired by Lena Ashwell

ELEN LEWIS
A Gentler Feeling

Red Stone Dancer – he sculpts,
Because sometimes, you have to carve out what
    you feel to understand life.
He's a young bear. Eyes burning, he dances
    tango with Sophie.
He takes her name – Brzeska,
Because sometimes, you have to carve in how
    you feel to understand love.
He's a flared match. Pencil scratching, he scrawls
    150 drawings in one life class.
He's a brave soldier. Shells bursting, he shapes a
    female figure from an enemy rifle,
Because sometimes you have to carve what you
    know, not what you see,
To express a gentler feeling,
He makes a Red Stone Dancer.

Inspired by Henri Gaudier-Brzeska

SAMANTHA CHAPLIN
Today the enemy

Today the enemy.
Woken by a brandy sore, makeshift pillow-ache
and the remembrance of his predicament.
Yesterday a Count, a prize-giver, now displaced,
alone in the hours, in the shadows; torn from
his English dream. He looks no one in the
eye, for him an oddity. He passes through
towns, head down, finding only the blind
eye of the hollyhocks in the cracks. Wealth
devalued, lineage lost, no longer welcome no
longer worthy. Fear propels him, tomorrow an
illegal alien? His mind travels the road that leads
back, tomorrow a prisoner? Yesterday a society
president, employer.
But today the enemy.

Inspired by Count Conrad Hochberg

MANDY LEE

Canary

These, our days
much longer now
for women who fight
through piles of washing
to Kensington Road
on multiple roads
to the factory bench.
Machine work, men's work?
Hard work, 'good' works.
Atten-shun!

Doing my bit
in overalls.
No metal allowed
a sparking risk
while shells I twist.
Turn, fill, and pour
add, tap and finish
TNT.
Pray we don't explode.
Fire!

We are Canaries
singing through the shifts.
Back on the road
to family at home.
Skin dyed yellow
poisonous.
Halt!

No final salute.
Boxed and ended
unrecognised.
Small hushed deaths
for women who fight.
These, our days.

Inspired by Charlotte (Lottie) Mead

JOHN JORDAN

Business Log: July 18, 1919

My bloodstained shirt tells me I have a
quandary: Chuckie. When sober, he's a top
mechanic, probably our best. By late afternoon,
he's often neither. And usually asleep. Today's
first six hours counted without incident. Shortly
after three, I hear shouting from Service.
Investigating, I see Chuckie, Ben Swanson
and Charles Z scuffling. The latter two woke
up the former with three gallons of water.
The Great War came flooding back through
Chuckie with rage. Ben's face paid the price.
This quandary tests my leadership and my
compassion more with each day.

Damn that war. And damn my bloodstained shirt.

Inspired by Felix J. McShane

JILL HOPPER
Dead Man's Pennies

In the hand, two red discs,
Stamped with the names of brothers
Killed five weeks apart at the Somme.
They weigh almost nothing –
Tom's bent and discoloured,
Sam's intact, still on its length of string.
Their mother kept them all her life,
Along with their medals and the scrolls sent by
    the King,
And the cardboard tube that the scrolls came in.
Sleepless each night, the question she kept
    asking was:
How were their tags saved and their bodies not?
Where do my sons lie?
In silence she received the nation's answer:
Memorial coins, heavy and cold in the hand.

Inspired by Sarah Hyde

LUCY FLETCHER

To an isolated theatre of war

Distanced from dreams.

Caught in a war that ceased, yet his battles far
from eased.

From working down the pit at 13 with ponies
breathing down his neck.

To a tent-less, frost-bitten camp in Salonika,
hardened by the chill's remorseless gnawing at
numb fingers.

To building roads in bleak lands,
dragging tired feet alongside mules shouldering
dwindling supplies.

The enemy blowing fire and fury. Stranded in a
distant theatre of war.

Frozen in time; on standby for seasons and
hostilities to thaw.

Isolated from his family and future wife,
for 2 years, 11 months and never-ending days.

Distanced from dreams.

Inspired by James Wood

BECCA MAGNUS
Forgot My Socks

A scant candle lights the measure of this letter.
My blasted pen leaks; feral words scurry forth.
Our lines break. My own refuse. Language flees.
Braver than I.

I forgot my socks. Left them at the rest camp.
A trivial thing, socks. Morning greets us with
bone-shattering salutations, an iron hail, hailing
the end to us. The mulching masses. From
stand-to to stand down, all I think of are my
unheeding heels. I cannot stand to stand without
socks. Sock it all.

My words blunted, another letter stunted.
One by one, snuffed out. The last sputters of
a scant candle.

Inspired by Isaac Rosenberg

GEMMA CANTELO

One of One

28 January 1917.
One of sixteen million.

One sister of war
To rest in Malta's sacred keeping.

One of seven
Brigaded by the Lady of the Black Horse
To bring hope to wounded ground.

Of these doctors how many would return?

A rallying cry from Hunter Street!
One of forty-eight
Bugles raised in reply and shipped to serve.

One should be taken and the other left?

To serve, to heal, to die with men
Laid to dust in Pieta.
One of fifteen hundred.

At the graveside assembled the Lady Doctors.
One sister of war.

One of one.
28 January 1917.

Inspired by Dr Isobel Addy Tate

SEAN JULLIARD

Young Horace Iles

Young Horace Iles, a choirboy
A child at just fourteen
Fresh of face but his build and strength
Would pass him for eighteen

He suffers the shame
Of a white feather
Given to him on the tram

It's time to do your duty, Horace
It's time to be a man

No coward, Horace signs up:
Private, The West Yorkshire Regiment
He lied about his age

Then away to France
To the Somme
And the mud and the blood and the bombs
No place for a man
No place for a child
But there's no way home for young Horace Iles

Inspired by Horace Iles

AMANDA EDMISTON

Watching Scotland's Waves

Lost at sea: there is one possible explanation to
1917's missing diary – snatched by a Kelpie?

Traveller, renaissance writer, organiser of The
Scottish Women's Suffrage Movement, but her
diaries merely relate domesticity!

Then, in 1918, 'Memoranda: Will went down on
Laurentic Jan 1917'. HMS Laurentic sank. On
board, 350 men and a hold full of gold bullion.

Florence surely aware of the prescient nature
of folklore, later relates ancient beliefs that
Hebridean sailors lost beneath leaden-waves will
always return home.

Brother Will's body found on island-shore, home
to Holm, 6 months later.

Many lives and £22,000,000 lost at sea.

Inspired by Florence Marian McNeill

[73]

LUCY BEEVOR

Botanical

'In the wound? Moss?'
'Yes,' the petite Englishwoman asserts.
'Sphagnum. Four times more absorbent
than cotton wool; antiseptic; abounds in
Ireland's bogs; a network of volunteers
will harvest, send to our depot in Dublin
to be sewn into dressings.'

In the greenhouse she tends her husband's
    seedlings.

The War Office declares it an official dressing;
    'Let's sphag!'

Youngest brother, fearless Ted, falls at Loos.

As Dublin rises she slips through barricades,
    distributes dressings under fire.

Hepaticas and iris reticulata bloom.

The Somme. Depot busier than ever.

By Armistice, 905,600 dressings dispatched.

However she can she puts moss in the wound.

Inspired by Elsie Henry

JAMIE DELVES

Autumn '18

Rome is falling,
Mein Schatz.
An infant empire already in decline.
Room's back to haven status.
No creases
        in the sheets.

Hard boiled,
Tightly wound;
Hoping to be
Homeward bound.

Miracles are chimerical,
Weltanschauung with serpent's tail.

Impetuous cadet,
With an allergy to authority,
Flexing
     obstreperously.

Why not hog?
Ganzes Schwein.
Take things. Get ahead.

(Burgeoning emergencies)

Salute the crisis,
Solution on the iris,
bone dry
dead slow,

– Flee with the zaftig pharaohs –

Quashing nausea,
Helpless, hopeless…

Barrel-chest beating,
sending panthers by sea to west Africa,
I roll instead of fight, I'm afraid.

Old Otto the autocrat,

Rome is falling.

Inspired by Hans Richard Joachim Von Volkmann

TONI STUART

the unarmed soldier: remembering the cape coloured corps

I East Africa
bastaard hottentot. coloured. kleurling. but the
soldier is unnamed. the soldier is unarmed. his
arms carry stretchers. his arms build bridges and
drive patrol cars. the soldier is wading through
swamps in heavy rains. the soldier is malaria
fevering his body. the soldier is repatriated.

II Egypt and Palestine
the soldier is armed. bastaard hottentot.
coloured. kleurling. but the soldier is just a
soldier. the soldier is taking Square Hill: 181
prisoners and an enemy field gun. paving
Allenby's road to Damascus: towards defeat
of the Ottoman Empire. bastaard hottentot.
coloured. kleurling. but the soldier is unnamed.

Inspired by the Cape Coloured Corps

HANNAH RILEY
Peace needs work

Peace needs work.

And my work is stories.

Stories told through a lens and printed in sepia.
Stories of wounded bodies, fanned out beneath
an incongruously theatrical canopy.
Stories of a building that echoes the glorious
colour of home (or so they say).
Stories of 'our father the King-Emperor'
offering his words of support in their mother
tongue.

We must reject aggression, avoid conflict,
my father said.

But pacifism does not lead to peace.
Peace needs positive action.
The bolstering of a national mood.
The drive towards a carefully engineered
conclusion via a series of captured moments.

Peace needs work.

Inspired by Allen H. Fry

PHILIP PARKER

Goodnight Kiss

Five strides apart, five summers past, I saluted
you and the old sweats riding to War.

I fell first. And waited: while you mined the
frozen mud. Ducked into crump holes. Pinched
lice from your seams. Felt the pear drops' sting
at Wipers.

You drink Hannah's words from home;
Jimmy's walking now.

Then you're following the tank tracks from
Cambrai. The chase draws you to Mons, where
your War began. In the woods on the eleventh
day, a goodnight kiss. Ninety minutes to
Armistice.

My wait ends. First and last in a bunker for pals,
we lie five strides apart.

Inspired by George Edwin Ellison

KATIE-ROSE COMERY

Unannounced

A shaking hand lifts knocker. Lets it fall.

Madness, really: two days' leave, first and last for
months, and he comes here. Not home to sister,
father, mother, like other men. A chance trip to
an unknown house. Chance knock, hoping he'll
answer.

Worth it, though: to see the face of the man who
wrote *Ma mère l'Oye*. Hands that found notes for
Daphnis et Chloé.

A name learnt in earlier days, fingers fumbling
on piano keys. *Ra-vel.*

He hears footsteps now, heartbeat quickens.
Sound of bolt sliding, door opens. Smile opens.
In greeting, he reaches out a shaking hand.

Inspired by Stuart Fletcher

STEPHEN BARNABY

C. Blythe
Spin Bowler

Twists and turns.

Known universally as Charlie, strong Cockney
accent, left school before turning thirteen, joined
his father in the engine workshops at Woolwich
Arsenal.

Christened Colin, talented violinist (lessons paid
for by his father), beautiful left arm spinner for
Kent and England, subtle, imaginative, lethal.

But what is lethal?

Slight, boyish, plagued by seizures triggered
by stress.

Deemed fit for service with the King's Own
Yorkshire Light Infantry.

Killed at Ypres, November the 8th 1917, a piece
of shrapnel passing through his wallets, defacing
the photograph of his wife Janet, going on
to pierce his heart.

Twists and turns.

Inspired by Charlie Blythe

TOM COLLINS
The voice of a blackbird

He was born in a blackbird's nest, blessed
by poetry. Like Rhiannon's fabled birds
his words could sing the dead to life
and mesmerise the living.
As Gallipoli unfurled he embraced

Crocknaharna's pearl.
In Serbia he feasted on blue cherries.
Hospitalised in Egypt, a blackbird
materialised in his troubled mind.
Liffey was his Rubicon.

British soldier or Irish Volunteer?
The Rising transfigured him.
McDonagh's ghost claimed him.
The King held him to his duty. Flanders,
not Ireland, was his martyr's soil.

Bittern and blackbird cried
as the Germans' shell
fell.
But he was someplace else,
back where he was born.

Inspired by Francis Ledwidge

VIVIEN JONES
Little Is Known

Little is known of Jessie, the youngest sister, save
that she died of dysentery in Salonika, far, far
away from wee grey damp Dalbeattie. A staff
nurse in a tent city in a wild climate, hair frozen
to her pillow, a man's greatcoat for warmth, the
madness of stinging insects exchanging blood for
illness, a world of vomit and diarrhoea, of broken
men and boys, an army of women looking upon
horror determined to mend what they could. A
grave in Kalamaria, her name on memorials in
Edinburgh and Dalbeattie; no story, no legend.
We regret so *little is known*.

Inspired by Staff Nurse Jessie Jane Paterson

JANE BERNEY

White Lie

What they did.

What they did to the horses.

That went to bloody war.

Six weeks sardined on ships; one way ticket to
    mud and guts.

Heroes without a prayer.

He'd seen the papers.

Knew the rules.

One from every farmer.

This 'one' was going; over his dead body.

As a boy they'd coursed through his veins.

Deceit was not his nature.

And yet.

When Captain Herbert came to his gate,
    no conscripts were to be seen on Berney's farm.

Just a scrawny beast silhouetted by bush.

'House cow.'

In his nightmares they reared their jagged heads.

What they did.

Inspired by John Hanson Berney

RICHARD PELLETIER

Én vagyok a mondot álom*

Someone whispered '*Kertesz*'
and the finger trembled –

the violinist played blind –
the gypsy children kissed naked at Esztergom
the blackandwhite century
millions killed and maimed
frozen on thin silver halide fields.

Like all great romantics, exiled –
to love the Paris light
and the long dark shadows of the world.
The *Leica*; charcoal, lightning, dream
Elizabeth.

Our sweet loneliness became his –
chairs of Paris, Mondrian, Montmartre
Satiric Dancer.
Wounded soldiers swim –
fire and poppies in their wake.

The night
the Village,
bony finger
steel shutter
Still bitter, still *seeing* her, would *anyone* remember?
Where was she now, *Elizabeth*?
Someone whispered '*Kertesz*'

Inspired by the photographs of Andre Kertesz
*Hungarian: I am the dream told

WENDY JONES

Laura

Your brother Arthur. That's how he signed off.
Never much one for writing, his last letter just
a postcard, 'Right is Might' embroidered on the
front.

Then the telegram, closed curtains, Mother
red-eyed all day, Father drinking not talking.
You cry too, but not for long. You're needed.
The WAAC wants women as cooks and clerks
and mechanics. You'll go for Arthur. He fought –
you'll cook – for England.

Behind the lines, peeling a million potatoes.
But there are jokes and laughter and learning to
parley-voo. In truth, the best time of your life.
He'd smile, he would. Your brother Arthur.

Inspired by Laura Leavesley

JOHN BURWELL

Bissonnet Street

No one remembers the boy – the dogfighter
    apparent –
or the splintered wreck of his final exercise.

One in twenty thousand to join. One in ten to
    die training.
One among millions to dream they might end
    the war.

The war did end, but his victory was no brighter
    or warmer
than the ghosts of his friends.

The millionaires on 'Poor Farm Road' were
    relieved
when their street received his name.

Now, millions of drivers navigate a map of the
    dead,
the dim aspirations of their blind routines

tracing arcs across a death roll,
names of lost boys no one remembers.

Inspired by George Herman Bissonnet

JAMIE JAUNCEY

Hunters

Five white ferrets
He clambers up companionways
To their hutch, high aft
And feeds them morsels
From the mess
The chirruping cheers him
As they steam southeast from Scapa
Hunting the Hochseeflotte

Later, as the fire gong rings
Ting, ting, pause, ting
In number four gun turret
The months of drill kick in
He's twenty-three
And *Agincourt's* guns are roaring

Come dawn the sea's a Sargasso
Of hammocks, decking, lifebelts
8,600 souls lost, 175,000 tons sunk
And the hutch gone, splintered

Days later, fat on rats
And one coal black
From hunkering in a bunker
They re-appear
Five white ferrets

Inspired by Angus Cunninghame Graham

HEATHER ATCHISON

Plus ça change

Picture the hands
Of a little black boy
Pocketed
On the run from snarling hatred
Clenching his way
Towards freedom
In another country

Picture the hands
Of a machine gunner
Fumbling over steaming metal
Dealing death in Europe's trenches
Protecting mud brothers

Picture the hands
Of a fighter pilot
Threading clouds above France
Dancing his wings
Duelling
      and

          diving

Picture the hands
Of a white-haired elevator operator
Gloved fingers on buttons
Yes, ma'am.

Two hands.
One man.

Embraced by one nation
For his unrelenting courage

Rejected by another
For nothing more
Than the pigment in his skin

Picture the hands.

Inspired by Eugene Bullard

PETER NOONE

At Mannequin Hill

At Mannequin Hill where boys are sent to die,
Where bombs explode and blow them all to bits,
Limbless bodies scatter and surround
The gunless man inching towards the cries
Of barely breathing bodies screaming: 'Mum.'
Trenches filled with Tommies yet to die
Shout: 'Don't worry lads, our Bill'll bring you back.'
Deaf to bombs and bullets, blind to barbed wire,
Through mud he crawls to save the not-quite-deads,
To patch them up and send them out again.
For courage in the face of carnage,
On Bill they pinned a Victoria Cross
For bringing back our boys at Mannequin Hill.

*Inspired by William Coltman, VC, DCM and Bar,
MM and Bar*

MICHAEL LONGLEY

Citation

Father's Military Cross:
The citation divides into lines:
'For conspicuous gallantry and devotion to duty
In leading the waves of his company in a raid
And being the first to enter both objectives
In spite of a severe shrapnel wound in the thigh.
After killing several of the enemy himself,
He directed the fire of his Lewis gunners
And rifle bombers on to a working party
Of over one hundred of the enemy, and controlled
The mopping-up of the enemy dug-outs.'
Kept alive by his war cry and momentum,
I shiver behind him on the fire-step.
Father's Military Cross.

Inspired by Captain Richard Longley, MC

PAUL WHITE

Stop Fighting Children

Stop fighting children
I shouted
Some days when I came
Across a scuffle in the classroom
And instantly they'd freeze
At the words of their headmaster
But now I'm giving orders
Sent out by those
Who should know better
Than to waste the
Young lives I'm sent to muster
I'll blow my whistle tomorrow
Reminding me
Of the call to playtime sports
And this lot will all get set
Jump up and pelt headlong
Across a field
Toward a barbed wire finishing line
That's just another lie
Because there'll be no end to it
Until both sides
Stop fighting children

Inspired by Kenneth Robert White

SINÉAD KEEGAN

A Soldier's Pistol

Sinne Fianna Fáil.

> The wild rebel countess kissed her gun
> when memories of Lissadell's tenants called
> put on the freedom fighters' trousers
> held the sniper's line in St. Stephen's Green

> kissed her gun under the white flag
> traded her Mauser for a court martial
> an Irish soldier ready to stand
> in the stonebreaker's yard
> her life for her country

> kissed her gun
> but woman's hands had pulled the trigger
> so she was left to stand
> as the sixteen fell
> her voice defiant rose

> kissed her gun and sang
> march we triumphant living or dying
> Ireland to free

Soldiers are we.

Inspired by Countess Constance Markievicz
(née Gore-Booth)

SALLY HARPER

The List

To do today.

Light the range. Keep out the cold.
Give Maud and George their porridge.
Feed Henrietta, see if she's laid.
Go to the grocer; potatoes, kippers, split peas,
    Coal Tar soap.
Boil up the bones.
Help mum on the beer tent, new recruits are in.
    Poor buggers.
Pay the rent.
Meet Nora down *The Rosemary*. Tell her what
    Ruby said about Doris, cheeky mare.
Write to Charles.
Write to Cliff.
Check the lists. You've got to look girl.
Chop wood.
And don't look up, don't look up.
The baby killers are coming back.

Bleeding hell.

To do today.

Inspired by Alice Limpus

BEVERLEY MOORE

Safe on shore

We didn't talk. We just drank. And we left
sharpish as the singing started. When Danny
Ryan's belting out *God save Ireland*, O'Grady's is
no place for the English.

A U-boat had picked the ships off one by one.
On watch down at the signal station, I'd taken
the first SOS, spent the morning relaying the
flood of messages. The live bait squad, they'd
called the patrol. Three knackered cruisers.
2,200 men. Lots of them coastguards, newly
mobilised by those fools at the admiralty.

Back at the cottages, we said goodnight. Gertie
opened the door, made tea. We didn't talk.

Inspired by Harry Turner

MIKE GOGAN

Jack Gogan, tea-taster, Dublin, 1916.

King nor Kaiser. When rebellion brewed, the
tea-taster volunteered for Irish freedom at Roe's
Distillery (did he sip?). I heard a kid spilled
the beans, 'There's the bloody rebel stuck the
bayonet in the Bobby's backside.'

A funny taste of war.

Less to stomach next: Interrogated. Court-
martialled. Sentenced to the firing squad.
Commuted to prison. Kicked head first into
the hold of a cattle ship. The back injury
that hastened his death at 52, a confectioner.
Bitter British justice.

I can taste a second's delay in the pull of an
espresso. Cheers Jack!

He served Ireland. Neither King nor Kaiser.

Inspired by Jack Gogan

TRACY JO BARNWELL

Snow

The snow begins to fall. An hour ago
a thousand curious eyes peered
from the Halifax shore. Two collided
ships split and sparked. Now shattered hulls

still burn, and along the fractured streets
the living ferry the dead from one wrecked pile
to another. No words tell it.
Utter desolation. All dead –

bodies, arms, etc. floating in the water.
Nothing is enough. But who will say it
if not me? The doctors and nurses
of Halifax tend the burning heart of Europe.

Here the wind must sing the dying to sleep.
Tonight I will write. And now the snow begins.

Inspired by Frank Baker

SUE EVANS

On his birthday

Owd Tat says...

No! Herr Hollweg. No! Herr Haeckel!!
Him you do not congratulate,
this man of 89 years.
You curs who give children poisoned sweets,
unleash Guytrash and Skriker upon the Earth,
deliver the Hun to Paris, to the very gates!

Brain whizzing like a scopperil,
Tat's memory retraces each departed son.
Where they have gone,
their forms and faces.
Lancashire lads, their bodies undone.

He will yet sing of triumph over Amalek,
of Justice.
Kaiser Bill's exile: ARMISTICE!
Ending the fearful slaughter, shattering
    Freedom's yoke.
The boys to Hurstwood come home post-haste,
OH, YES SIR!!

Owd Tat says...

Inspired by Tattersall Wilkinson

TAMARA O'BRIEN

Old English Women to Shoot

To be saved, I must have no hate in my heart.

A proper, whip-smart matron, sharp as a
   hospital corner.
No mercy for a nurse two minutes late for supper.
But angel to a tommy trapped behind the lines
   in Belgium.

Don't send me any more, she wrote. I am
   exhausted.
But, if anyone should die… keep sending them.
   We'll try.

And when they tied her, teary, to the stake,
In her worn blue suit, and hat with the
   tortoiseshell pin,
She bowed before the rifles, upright to the end.

I can't stop while there are lives to be saved.

Inspired by Nurse Edith Cavell

JOHN J SILLS

First World Problems

John James Sills
Aged 35
Lives in London
Supports Arsenal
Works as a milk carrier
Enlists in Marylebone, and leaves his family for
    two years
Fights for his life with three million others in the
    cold, crowded trenches of the Somme
Died in the great war so that we may have life

Goes onto Twitter to express his outrage and anger
Fights for a seat with five million others on the
    hot, crowded underground
Travels to Marylebone, and leaves his family for
    a few hours
Works as a management consultant
Supports Arsenal
Lives near London
Aged 35
John James Sills

Inspired by John James Sills

ANDY MILLIGAN

Love lost. Life gained.

The wedding invitation held a name not known,
a name repeated on the later telegram;
four months from blessing to bereavement.

A love she hid from her loves to come
in the attic pages of her pocket book.

A love turned to human mulch
on shellsunk ground,
impossible to find.

Until I traced, as she never did,
the meticulous record of sacrifice
to the site of his obliteration.

Standing where he fell, I understood
how I exist because he died.

Nearby was his memorial
and silently, beside his name, to honour
a love now known, I held the wedding invitation.

Inspired by Second Lieutenant Robert Bowran

SUSANNAH HART

Sister Currier

He gave me no face. Oh, yes, a name
and, yes, a uniform, and, even, yes,
my title: Sister. But where my face should be
a smudge, a blur. Behind us in the harbour
the boats are featureless, buildings merged
to one flat memory. Perhaps he wanted to erase
the heat, the flies, the specificity of pain. Yet
the shadows on Nurse Billam's apron almost shine.
My cape is crisply drawn. Perhaps he only saw
my rank, my purpose, and me a worker
in the great machine of war. And still the painting's
here. Perhaps that's what he gave me.

Inspired by Sister Florence Currier

CAROLINE HOPPER

A Suffragette joins the Women's Police Service

Her police report captures:
'Sallow, brown-haired suffragette,
Commits malicious damage to public art treasures.'
Special Branch is watching her.

But now she watches women
As they stir nitric acid in with sulphur.
She searches their khaki pockets and sleeves
For buttons and sweets, which don't mix well
   with TNT.

She watches women march by two
In Union Jack-draped coffins.
Her hair cropped short, her suit dark-blue,
Their faces sulphur-yellow.

She wasn't there to watch when Pembrey burned –
To see the shells rip through. But that malicious
   damage,
And the lives it took to manufacture,
She captures in her police report.

Inspired by Clara Mary Lambert

RAPH ADAS

Mary U Ful A Grase

WW1 Artillery drap brap
In-de Carribbean We-tink a earthquake
Mary! Tel de acesta war bruk-out

U-trang Oman a Kolor
U-kross front line Crimean-war
Fe-kare soja-mata chop-dem-up an-dem no meat
Dem duppy a cal-u fe warm klose an-shelta

U-face wars an-tan-tall wid dignety
Det tek 8 a mi-fambily-memba! No-warnin
Me tek a page out-a book
Nus-fala u xample nèer an far

Hail-up fram u-homlan JA – topa blu mounten
mi-deh
U-stat-U a St Tamas Aspital a testamony
A-salute-all warria bredren an sistren
WW1 a celabrate 100 – we-cah-fegot
Dem-gib life fe-we deh yah
Mary! U-Ful-A-Grase – Oman a-run de worl WW1

Inspired by the Jamaican BWIR nurses

FRANCESCA BAKER

To go home

To go home would be a relief. Away from here,
and its brittle battle bangs. Cracking snaps in
my fractured head. Flickering whacks against
the bank. Broken limbs and breaking mind.
Shooting rams of shattering bullets. Head in
shatters, body battered. Never ending, brain
bending, guns firing through every hour. Flames
burn and rage, trapped in a cage – no, way, out.
Dark days and black nights, the only light is the
angry fire of death. The world in disarray. Like
dominoes, they fall. Like slugs, we crawl. My
mind is splintered. My body crushed. I want to
go home.

Inspired by Francis Henry Dutton

SAM KNOWLES

Almost

'Must be proud?' offered the rector, blessing the Lewes War Memorial.

John Henry Crock snorted, indignant: 'Proud?'

His eyes traced the names of four of his five sons.

Samuel, Thomas, William, George.

George.

Almost.

France, on a hazy morning. September 1918.

Lance Corporal George Crock snatches a moment of calm midst the maelstrom of the Hundred Days Offensive, writing a letter to his wife in Sussex.

Out of the autumn sky, no warning. A shell shreds the silence. The shell ends George's war, his life.

'Proud? If my sons were standing here with me I would be. Must be proud!'

Inspired by Lance Corporal George Crock

077

ROWENA ROBERTS

Unwritten: Conflict in a dugout grave

My dear Nellie.
I linger for eternity on
My final thoughts.
The shriek and thunk of skull-shredding shells –
    these are not
What I should tell you. My surroundings,
Without doubt,
Reveal absolute evil. So I know,
I cannot just
Speak truth to you,
Though you wanted me to
Throughout this war.
My suffering
Obliterated
My life's joy, my love for you and Duncan,
In this dugout – now my resting place.
I dreamt simple dreams
And yet,
Today I am gone, my plans were all in vain.
I regret my life.
You'll never hear me say these words,
My dear Nellie.

Read from top to bottom, then bottom to top.

Inspired by George Gurnel Davison

STEPHEN POTTS

Dismounted

Briefly? A horseman.

1899   Barefoot Shankill boyhood.   *Victoria*

1910   Da's Titanic engines –   *Edward*
       But no shipyard life for me.

       Though still I hear the rivets.

1912   An army horse in Ireland: uniform   *George*
           and gun.

1914   Words? A man of few.
       'I punched the holes in doughnuts,' all
           I say.

       Though still I hear the bullets.

1916   Horseless, behind Ypres machine guns.

1918   In London, wounded, when peace bells
           rang.

1919   Pip, Squeak & Wilfred on my
           Contemptible chest.

Later   A policeman's lot in Ireland: uniform
           and gun.

       Though still I hear the hooves,
       I was – all too briefly – a horseman.

Inspired by Lance Corporal David Shields McNally

JEROME CAIN

The Black Death

Young black man. Red cap.
Ignore their sniggers, you're in the 369th.

Tentative steps on French soil.
'Salut mon ami!'
Warm voices. Equals.

Then, sentry duty. Henry and Needham sit.
Ears prick to a wire-cutters clip.
Bullets rip. Needham slips.
Shrapnel shreds, shrapnel nips.
Rifle jams. Out comes knife.
To save young Needham, Henry takes four lives.

Heroes parade. Cheers. Waves. But what did
     they say to disability pay? Not today.
Wife left, took the kids, Henry hit the bottle.
Buried at 32: alone and forgotten.

Not by us, not today.
Your life was not in vain.
Young black man.

Inspired by Sergeant Henry Johnson

BRIDGET WATERS

In arduis fidelis*

Remember golden summers of haymaking
and a great peace of heart? Old Boys, twins,
Olympians. Tennis lawns and bicycling.

Now all ease and carelessness is gone.

The strains of a waltz played on a pianola, from
a partly shattered house. The zip, zip of bullets
hitting sandbags. Mercifully numbed, or who
would ever smile here?

Mender of men, wounded sick wild things
muddied to the eyes. Amidst the brutal mess
of war, yours the care and cure of bodies instead
of souls.

In arduis fidelis. You fetched them home.

We will remember you for valour. Do you
remember golden summers?

Inspired by Captain Noel Godfrey Chavasse, VC & Bar, MC
*'In arduis fidelis' is the motto of the Royal Army Medical
Corps (RAMC). It means 'faithful in adversity'

ELISE VALMORBIDA

Two Sides

My two grandfathers
fight
The War in Snow and Ice.
It's not
The Great War.
It's not
The First World War –
they don't know
there'll be another.

In Italian, there are
two verbs
for knowing.
A person: *conoscere*.
A fact: *sapere*.
But history and story are
one word:
storia.
It is all the telling of tales.

I have a medal. A
voluptuous winged
victory
for every Italian soldier.
On one side
it says (I translate):
THE WAR
FOR ITALIAN
UNITY
1915–1918.

On the other side:
CAST IN
ENEMY BRONZE.

They live
(I live)
to tell the tale,
my two grandfathers.

Inspired by my two grandfathers

DAVID BATY

Below the front

Below the front, a wall of cloud climbs high
above the hill, black billows hide what light
there was, then crack. A flash and orange bloom,
as waves tear up the track. Wind whips the hail
and hurls its rage, no place to be up top.
Down deep, the tunnels drive towards the ridge.
Clay kickers, miners, dig on, and whisper.
Silent canary wisps stand watch over
muted shovels, spoiled bags overladen,
busted props shouting to catastrophe,
close quarters just a wall and life away.
Others' noise cold comfort, silence a fuse,
no one should be alone below the front.

Inspired by William Hackett VC

JAN DEKKER

Two times nein

A trench, France, 1917

MAJOR: So, a Sturkopf!* (*Drawing pistol*) Attack.
  Or I'll shoot you.

HERMAN: (*meeting his gaze*) I'd rather die quickly
  here than slowly out there.

(MAJOR *pauses, shaken, silent.*)

Hermann's home, Westphalia, 1955

HERMANN: He made me groom his horse, and
  count bodies. Lucky. 100 men went from here.
  Only me and another returned, and he's blind.
  But we both see everything in our nightmares.

JOSEF: The second war?

HERMANN: By 1944, they wanted men my age.
  I said no again. So stubbornness saved my neck.
  They say it's Westphalian. But I learned it in a
  trench… France.

Inspired by Hermann Steven
German: a person who's pigheaded, or stubborn

MICHELLE NICOL
White ribbons

Just another soldier
Returning from… someplace else.

Where was I?

How did chisel, plane and saw
Become rifle and Lewis gun?
When did grease, oil and sand
Replace sawdust?

My feet fall on cold stones.
Where am I?

Home, they tell me, home.

Swan girls, grown like weeds, sail into sight.
Smooth grain emerging in shafts of winter light.
Sharp starched Sunday best.
I fight to remember… and forget.

Where was I when the Zeppelin came?
Why does the little one hide behind her sister
    mother?

Bullets strike from the mouths of babes.
'That's not my daddy,
He's just another soldier.'

Inspired by John Robert Anderson

HENRIETTA McKERVEY
In Search of Kingsley

Fourteen days gone. Absence recorded in hours, minutes, seconds. Days are now too vast, too wearying to count. The world moves ever-forward, yet I am turning in the contrary direction, with no ability to right myself. The war is won, my son is lost.

He is no longer moving to the sound of the weary barrel-organ that grinds out the tunes of human life, material life. But loss in the noumenal world becomes profit in the other realm. In spirit, I will find him. Today, November 15th, he would have been twenty-five. He is twenty-five. He is fourteen days gone.

Inspired by Sir Arthur Conan Doyle

MARTIN LEE

Marjorie Cornell

She couldn't be feeling safer.
Enveloped by brothers,
Safeguarded by parents,
She hasn't a care in the world.

1912, alive in the moment,
Marjorie smiles for the camera
almost as young as the century,
as full of potential.

Not needing to conceive of the future
where her reflective grandson
posts this, now poignant
family photo on Facebook.

But no one else is smiling.

You can imagine that
they sense what we know
concerning what lies ahead.
For them, but also for her.

Could she be shielded from
the four brothers she'll lose,
the heartache she'll never lose?
She couldn't be.

Inspired by Marjorie Cornell

SOPHIE GORDON

Impression

One man's gift. To soothe, to heal, to honour –
peace.

Not poppies – waterlilies.

Battle within earshot, you stayed.
You found patriotism in your own garden.
Meditation in a million brushstrokes.
Solace in your work.

No blood, no mud, here.

Your response to trauma, sorrow, death?
Harmony, beauty, life
and light.

Canvases – big enough to swim in – flooded with
    colour and light.
Consuming vision in thick paint, drowning the
    senses.

A million eyes have bathed in your twelve
    paintings,
and not a ripple to be seen, only felt –
deeply.

Stirred beneath the surface
by a masterpiece, humbly offered.
One man's gift.

Inspired by Claude Monet

MONIKA LEHNER

The young survivor

The opening shots came from nearby her village on 29 July 1914. Vienna had declared war by telegram the day before.

An Austro-Hungarian citizen age five, living across the river from Belgrade, Rosina was undisturbed by these events. It took four childhood years for the scare of death to make its way to Rosina.

Soldiering in the battle for her life were doctors of a hospital set up against the invasion of Spanish Flu.

In November 1918 she was a feted survivor. Much later she became a refugee and then my grandmother, navigating ever-changing borders, far beyond the opening shots.

Inspired by Rosina Obrovski

DAVID & JORDAN BICKERTON

The lost boys of London

Letters of living-light calling men to the front
and wrapping them with prayer and care.
Powering on into the future, the gift of motion
branded through the ages. Those brave names
recorded and illuminated, ringing down among
the bells of the city fair.

How the town grows older and brighter in safety,
now that the battle's over and won. Casting a
net around so many Tiny Tims amid the smog,
caught up in the thick of the present. Each
and every patient worthy of attention, each
flake a thank you from the lost boys of London
in letters of living-light.

Inspired by Charles Cheers Wakefield

ROB BRIGGS

The Red Baron's Reflection

He must fall: The best English flying man.

Lone wolf of the skies, with nowhere to hide,
Forty-four men shot down and died.

Devoted to freedom, honour and country,
Does he not harbour resentment and cruelty?

Jagdstaffel 11 tore Bloody April,
A circus convened to kill and disable.

With paramount courage and well-weathered luck,
Defying his orders, five times he struck.

From a dogfight in cloud, chasing my brother,
We'll not fly again to fight one another.

But I will strive to be as good as I can,
To far exceed the best flying man.

Remember Ball: He must fall.

Inspired by Albert Ball, VC

IRENE LOFTHOUSE

Invisible Man

The grand daughter said, 'Invisible Man,
I know that you fought in the war.
But Private 241351,
It's hard to find out more.

Cairo? Gallipoli? Suez Canal?
Were you at the Somme?
Where, in 1917, did
The mustard gas come from?

"Buggered lungs", Gran said,
"Not wanted at t'works;
But laiked in t'pub wi his mates
Who understood his quirks."

Heard hushed chats at Gran's
About you ruining their life,
Whilst I looked t'postcards
You'd sent to your wife.

Robert of Lancashire Fusiliers,
Your war was full of slaughter,
A hidden history of the Invisible Man,'
Said the grand daughter.

Inspired by Private Robert Nuttall Lofthouse

ROGER MORRIS

The white feather

It sits within my palm,
As weightless as a wish,
White as a snowflake
Before it melts into a tear.
But this will not melt.

She would not cry for me,
She would not smile for me,
Though I was young
And she was pretty.

I close my hand
And it is gone.
But I feel it burning
Its white hot mark
Into my skin.

No kind words,
No gentle touch.
All she had for me
Was this token,
Not of love.
Of something cowering,
Crabbed and shivering,
Infinite inside me.
Of fear. It will not melt.
It sits within.

Inspired by Robert Grieves

JOHN ALLERT

Private Angel

My Private Angel,

I bring you the baked white light of Adelaide.
The lyrical warble of magpies.
The lilac flush of jacarandas.
That first frosty sip.
The eucalypts in February, astringent gum-filled air.
And the beery cheering of the terraces.

Let me take this milky gloom, this premature sunset.
The wittering of the sky-lark, deaf to this hell.
The viscous black crimson, of man inside out.
Caked cold fingers, clawing hot tin cups.
Kerosene stained water, wetting rigor-white lips.
The liquor of death, sweet cloying stench.

I trace the cold letters of your name.
My brother Les, my private angel.

Inspired by Leslie Angel

SUZIE INMAN

A dream that died

In another life you came home, love.
And our James knew his father.

You came home, still wearing the warm socks
you'd asked mother to knit and held us with
quiet relief. No trenches there.

But in this real life they sent home nothing. No
muddy details. No socks. No wedding band, my
forever Valentine.

If peace had soared sooner you could have
come back to me. And that other life might have
begun. Oh Canada!

I've lived my life. Loved our son fiercely. And I
didn't dream of much... except of you.

Coming home to us. In another life.

Inspired by Annie Barron

DAVID MATHEWS

Ddôl Germans*

'When we escape, Herr Lloyd, we need Welsh to speak?'

'Dan ni'n ildio,' said Lloyd, as he prepared his camera. 'We surrender.'

Soldier and sailor laughed, but linked arms for their picture, for the postcard home.

At the pharmacy, Kate – baby Hugh in her arms – had teased her husband as he set out once more. 'Photographing Germans in a whisky distillery. A deacon, you are. Careful, boy.'

Behind the camera, Lloyd learned about his subjects' battles, Neuve Chapelle, Heligoland, Dogger Bank. He learned, too, who shared his Calvinistic faith; should he pray for them?

'Perhaps, Herr Lloyd, when we escape.'

Inspired by H. W. Lloyd
Welsh: The Germans' Meadow

JONATHAN BARNES

Dead Marshes

The Dead Marshes, through which I sent my
halfling heroes, were meant as a memorial for
those whom I had left behind - bold warriors,
mighty in deed, felled and laid down in dark
water. While they slept, I was returned, wounded
and heart-sick, to the living. Years passed and
memory faded. I grew sleek and plump and
worldly. Gold and approbation were mine
though I had never sought them out. Yet for all
of my fortunate fame I understood that there
was a part of me which, like those fallen, had
never been permitted to leave the dead marshes.

Inspired by J. R. R. Tolkien

GITA RALLEIGH

Distant drums

Drums of war sound better from afar, they told me. I resolved to return as a hero, crossing dark waters to a strange land. Rations, wages and uniform beckoned poorer kin but I was a born soldier, Manta Singh, proud Subedar of 15th Ludhiana Sikhs. Now as the guns fall silent, soft ashes rain upon the many corpses afloat in these unholy trenches. I mourn all my mud-embalmed brothers locked in death's embrace, their creed and caste undone. Hai Rab! How swiftly God's name is torn from every steadfast tongue and buried beneath the thundering **drums of war**.

Inspired by Manta Singh

JOAN LENNON

Except...

Not the end – the beginning!

the beginning
        of the end
                of the World War wedge
all those boys' broken bodies
        driven between
                this Ontario farmboy
and his mission field

the shout that drowned out the call would be stilled
the start and the end would be stitched back together

except...

it was war there too,
        and the Chinese soldier,
                writhing on the table,
bled and sobbed just the same

except...

the stitches pulled
        and what oozed out pooled
                and festered in his mind
and the screams echoed

it was not...
it is not...
not the end

Inspired by James Mortimer Clark

SUE BURGE

Souvenons-nous

It's nearly over, thinks Augustin Trébuchon.
He doesn't know the men he's trusted for four
extraordinary years are barely pen-poised. He's
bait in one last battle, orchestrated to twist arms,
allay hesitation. Instead he dreams of verdant
Montchabrier, bright-yolked eggs, his long-ago
lambs – tough now, their wool finger-deep. He
itches to play his accordion, make the girls dance.

A lazy bullet arcs through grey air.

Augustin would frown if he could see his memorial
date – 10 November 1918 – '*Propaganda!*' He
knows he had an extra day to breathe. *In, out, in,
out, out, out, out… it's nearly over.*

Inspired by Augustin Trébuchon

FAYE SHARPE

The Unknown Warrior

Known unto God, whose face was this.
A face with numberless names,
as countless as the frozen tears of winter's
    first winds.
Conscripted from the grave to do my duty
    forever more,
I guard the crater left in every human heart by
    darlings disappeared;
That crypt smothered by the world's grief,
    gratitude and regret.
I am the changing yet constant story found in
    the flicker of a candle's flame,
a story that erupts from the tomb to scald sleep.
I remain to be remembered, to prick your eyes
    and conscience. Peace!
Whose face was this? A face known unto God.

Inspired by the Unknown Warrior

BIOGRAPHIES & CONTEXT

001 ANGUS GRUNDY

Angus Grundy moved to Prague over 20 years ago to become a writer. He now writes for brands internationally. He's (still) working on his first novel.

Everyone knows Archduke Franz Ferdinand's assassination triggered WWI. But what about the chauffeur who took the fatal wrong turn on the day? This is his story.

002 THERESE KIERAN

From XMG, lives in Belfast - mother, poet, IWC XBorders: Accord 2018 participant, co-creator of Death Box. Has words – will travel: en route reading, learning, writing.

Jeanne De-Neve, Belgian refugee who fled to Ireland. She and her two sisters taught embroidery and helped establish the Bel-broid lingerie factory in Monaghan town.

003 MIRANDA DICKINSON

Miranda Dickinson is the author of nine novels, six of which have been *Sunday Times* bestsellers. She has sold one million books worldwide, in fifteen languages.

The war put lives on hold – marriages started and then paused; new wives waiting for their husbands so they could have their wedding photograph taken.

004 JACOB SAM-LA ROSE

Jacob Sam-La Rose is a poet and creative technologist, deeply engaged with poetry's power to connect, communicate, deconstruct and transform. He facilitates poetry programmes for educational and cultural institutions.

Gershom Browne was the last-surviving Guyanese veteran, Eustace Phillips his fallen brother-in-arms, his life barely recorded. Gershom never succumbed to bitterness. 'Glad to go,' he said.

005 EZRI CARLEBACH

Ezri Carlebach started out as a bass player, then spent twenty years in public relations and corporate communications, and now writes, lectures and plays the mandocello.

The iconoclastic voice of Karl Kraus has become better-known in English recently through various translations and studies. His ethical and critical concerns are painfully apt today.

006 ED PRICHARD

Ed Prichard helps people find the right words, tone of voice and ideas to express their brand effectively and make it sing clearly through every communication.

'My great grandmother, lost in a fog of dementia, thirty years after the Armistice. Son died at Gallipoli, my gran sent into service. No way home.'

007 LUCY FURLONG

Lucy Furlong is a writer, poet and walking artist, who teaches and facilitates walking/writing workshops for all ages. She performs her work nationally. http://www.lucyfurlong.com

Annie Kenney, working-class suffragette on the executive of the WSPU, arrested for shouting 'Votes for Women' at Manchester's Free Trade Hall - these are her words.

008 SOPHIE OLSZOWSKI

Sophie Olszowski is a medical writer with a beloved husband, cat, family, friends, running shoes, Jurassic Coast sea view and an occasionally-indulged love of writing fiction.

'World War One was to end them all. Harold Bing refused to fight. Wiser people than me say war is organised murder. Will we ever learn?'

009 DOUGLAS HOWATT

I'm a Dark Angel and copywriter in the Silicon Valley. Outside work, I still write, read and play with words. Oh, and I carve stone sculptures.

A woman breaks a gender barrier, inspires a country and leaves her mark on history. But history has left her no mark at all. Until now.

010 KARTIK KOMPELLA

Kartikeya Kompella is a brand consultant and author/ editor of books on branding. His first novel, a romcom, was launched in July 2018.

Principled. Natural. Uncluttered. Inspirational. Gandhi's ability to objectively decide the right course of action irrespective of popular sentiment was amazing and is inspirational to this day.

011 JOHN SIMMONS

Co-founder 26 and Dark Angels. Highly regarded business writer/ trainer. Has written the book(s) on brand writing. Novelist: next The Good Messenger (First World War background).

'Jessie Branch my widowed grandmother. Harry my grandad killed 1917, shot from a German plane. Jessie and Ce, babies then, became my mum and my aunt.'

012 STUART DELVES

Stuart Delves writes poetry, short fiction and copy. Since 2014 he has been writing booklets for Scottish Government commemorating WWI. Elsie Inglis' story bowled him over.

Still revered as a saint in Serbia and, back then, revered by thousands of the allied wounded and young Edinburgh mothers, this woman deserves a statue!

013 GILLIAN COLHOUN

Belfast native in a perpetual writing continuum of procrastination, agony and joy. Works with organisations, big and small, to express ideas worth sharing. Happiest when skiing.

Nursing was her vocation, but heroism is a position of the heart and Nurse Annie Colhoun faced down seventeen bombs to protect those in her care.

014 MAIA SWIFT

Maia is a freelance writer, namer and thinker from south-east London. She's written about everything from body butter to investment banking, mental health to mobile phones.

Over 35,000 women joined the wartime postal service. Violet Jackson was the postwoman in Trunch, Norfolk – a 'much-loved figure', carrying the most unimaginable weight every day.

015 CHARLOTTE MACKENZIE

Ex-journalist, digital writer and frustrated creative, Charlotte currently works in London. She has spent the last decade flitting between Colombia and the UK, writing, dreaming, exploring.

Photographer, explorer, woman ahead of her time. Olive Edis was a fearless creative and artist. Her work encapsulates the role of women on the front line.

016 OLLY DAVY

Freelance writer. Helping businesses communicate with precision and clarity. Flying the flag for plain English. Veteran of the War on Business Speak. Not sure who's winning.

'One of the many horrors my German great-grandfather survived as a teenage artillery officer on the Western Front was sadistic bullying by an unstable superior.'

017 HESTER THOMAS

Hester is a copywriter and trainer in writing skills for business people. Mostly enjoying retirement, she continues to work for a handful of much loved clients.

'As conscientious objectors were reviled, my family said nothing about Tom's role. An artist, he painted a portrait of a fellow 'conchie' - a story without words.'

018 ANN GORECKI

A parent, partner, daughter and lecturer, she also delves into hidden family history. Her 'work-a-day' writing is academic; unshackled, she usually writes short fiction, sometimes poetry.

Ettie Rout was a forward-thinking woman from New Zealand. Her practical, extensive war-effort was significant but, as it included promoting safer sex, was not universally appreciated.

019 TONY CLARKE

64-year-old family man, now retired after 36 years in public sector (housing and education), vegan, tweeter, twit, aspiring writer, serial-contributor to 26 projects.

Imperial War Museum. Amongst the more expected First World War exhibits – guns, uniforms etc. – sits a dog collar, adapted to carry messages. Research. Result: Richardson's Recruits.

020 GILLIAN MCKEE

Last 20 years spent persuading companies that doing good is good for business. Still trying. Need new stimulus. 26 projects keep my head and heart alive.

Youth, dreams, hope. The dawn of a new age. War came, youth went, dreams died, hope and potential drained away. Bright young things faded then expired.

021 RISHI DASTIDAR

Rishi Dastidar is head of verbal identity at strategic brand consultancy BrandPie, and also a poet - his first collection Ticker-tape is published by Nine Arches Press.

'Click. That's how easy it is to send a message. What if it wasn't? What if you had to risk death to deliver it? Would you?'

022 LISA ALLEN

I have a professional writing MA and 20 years of business writing experience, but it's the 26 projects that challenge and inspire me.

George Schmitt, 19, sailed to a new life in Australia. He died 8852 miles from Perth and just 148 from his family. All those miles, wasted?

023 MARGARET WEBSTER

Margaret Webster is a senior copywriter who writes large complex corporate communications. She also teaches people how to write compellingly so they can share their ideas.

'Mrs Beechey immediately came to my mind when I heard about the Armistice project. I remembered the story of her devasting loss and her incredible spirit.'

024 LISA ANDREWS

Freelance journalist, copywriter, editor, lifelong bookworm and stationery obsessive. Currently sending my first novel out to agents. Also co-editor of digital arts and literary magazine www.allthesins.co.uk

'Horace Sumner was my great-grandfather who served on several hospital ships. Family legend has it he saved a man from ending his life while on board.'

025 REBECCA DOWMAN

Rebecca Dowman is a writer, whippet-fancier, wild swimmer, wife, meditator, friend, boot sale enthusiast, Bruce Springsteen devotee, pro-refugee activist and Spurs fan. She lives in Arundel.

'This piece was inspired by the courage, pride and love evident in letters written by my subject, Leila Davies, about her brother Tal, a conscientious objector.'

026 ROBIN HARRIES

Robin Harries is a writer at communications and marketing agency Quietroom. He lives in London.

'Reginald was my great-grandfather. His military record was extraordinary and the war made him. It was the rest of his life that was a disaster.'

027 RONNIE MACKINTOSH

Ronnie's primarily a screenwriter with several produced short films and three optioned feature scripts, one of which is in pre-production. More can be seen at www. ronniemackintosh.co.uk.

'My centena is a fictional piece melded from stories of my great-uncle, Scots Guardsman John Mackintosh, and various written accounts of First World War experiences.'

028 SAMUEL CROSBY

Copywriter and digital creative. Smug Cornwall resident. Putting in a shift, helping brands to be braver. One or two short stories and poems doing the rounds.

Duke Kahanamoku – surfing's godfather – took surfing international during the First World War. Expecting comparisons between surfing and war, the research trail revealed a separate, human struggle.

029 JAYNE WORKMAN

An English writer now living and working in New Zealand, tackling the challenges of global branding during the week and an unruly 'lifestyle block' at weekends.

Margaret Wilson, engaged to Duncan who went to fight in Europe. Brother Arthur too. Words trickled through. Only Duncan returned. They married; he died at work.

030 NICKI LETTS

Nicki Letts is a writer and adventurer working from a '73 Kombi in Australia. From her moving desk, she seeks stories that take people places.

Gordon Naley enlisted, an Aboriginal. Against the rules – but he fought for a King who didn't recognise him as a citizen. Found mates in the trenches.

031 NEIL BAKER

Neil is a writer and communications consultant. He trains people to write better as a director of Dark Angels and is a board member of 26.

Jesse Robert Short was executed for his alleged role in the British Army mutiny at Étaples. He was a husband, a father and an innocent scapegoat.

032 CAROL McKAY

My motivation in writing is to explore and craft stories about individuals facing challenges thrown at them by society. I also write poetry and creative non-fiction.

'Who knows how we'd cope, faced with the emotional toll of global war. My centena pays tribute to working class people like my grandmother: survivors; rebuilders.'

033 BERT PREECE

Poggie in Chesterfield. Rob to the uni lot. Bert to most. At my best with a brief to beat, a story that needs to be told.

Mir Dast was an Indian soldier and Victoria Cross recipient. The poem's title is a Pashto proverb meaning: 'I am as good a man as you.'

034 LOU STEGGALS

Lou Steggals does comms/PR by day and stays sane with creative writing by night. This is her third 26 project (26 Writers in Residence, 26 Lies).

'I found Lena Ashwell through a bit of luck and being inspired by several music hall-related theatre projects I was working on including WW1-set Shakespeare.'

035 ELEN LEWIS

Elen is a writer, editor and ghostwriter. She writes novels about robots, lightning girls and foundling boys. She runs marathons slowly and plays the cello badly.

Henri Gaudier Brzeska could have been another Picasso if he hadn't died young. He was another flared match extinguished from promises, potential and all the might-have-beens.

036 SAMANTHA CHAPLIN

Currently writing my first novel whilst studying creative writing at the University of Oxford. The Count's butler in Somerset was my great great uncle, William Barrett.

Count Hochberg ignored all reproaches from the Kaiser for living in Somerset. The threat of war forced him to leave but his love for England endured.

037 MANDY LEE

Award-winning screenwriter and writer of other things, inspired by the things that drive us (and keep us stuck fast). Loves words - all of them.

Lottie Mead was a London munitions worker. Working with TNT shells slowly poisoned her, and she died in 1916 leaving four children and a husband behind.

038 JOHN JORDAN

I'm a copywriter by trade and a poet by hobby. Small details can tell stories. I look for those details and mine the stories behind them.

Discovery of a building that housed a once-famous automobile brand. The owner, a former sheriff, maintains dignity for all. A mechanic, scarred by war, presents challenges.

039 JILL HOPPER

Jill Hopper is a freelance writer for organisations large and small. Currently obsessed with narrative non-fiction, last year she wrote one book and read 92 others.

'Sarah Hyde was my husband's great-great-grandmother. She lost two sons at the Somme and their names are inscribed on the Memorial to the Missing at Thiepval.'

040 LUCY FLETCHER

Lucy Fletcher is a freelance copywriter and translator living in Edinburgh. Her writing is influenced by years spent working and travelling between Scarborough, Scotland and Spain.

'My centena is inspired by Private James Wood who was sent to Salonika. It reflects on his isolation, desperation and loneliness from being far from home.'

041 BECCA MAGNUS

Joyful rebel. Dreamer. Restless. Recklessly optimistic, she believes infusing business with beauty is a worthwhile thing. Freelance brand writer, graphic design dabbler, tea and biscuit enthusiast.

Isaac Rosenberg was an artist, poet and reluctant soldier. Searching for authentic expression, he discovered his powerful, gritty voice in the trenches he longed to escape.

042 GEMMA CANTELO

Gemma helps organisations communicate their ideas to politicians and the public. She has worked in the charity sector for 15 years, and writes mainly about health.

Isobel Addey Tate was born in Ireland to a merchant family. She was a medic in hospitals in Serbia and Malta, where she died in 1917.

043 SEAN JULLIARD

Sean is a London-based copywriter and content marketeer with a love for branding, golden-era advertising and carrying a heavy backpack up steep hills in the wintertime.

Recruitment officers would often turn a blind eye to any concern they had about age if a volunteer was passed fit to fight for his country.

044 AMANDA EDMISTON

Storyteller preoccupied with plants, aspiring to spill spoken words onto paper. Being part of the tale of a tiny WW1 lead-ship brought me to this shore!

'The daughter of an Orkney minister who travelled Europe, a suffragette, Scottish Renaissance-writer yet remembered for her recipe collecting. I elected to uncover her personal story...'

045 LUCY BEEVOR

Worked in the arts for 20+ years; her current focus is writing. Has zig-zagged the globe thanks to work, study and family; currently lives in Belfast.

Plant lover, society lady, who masterminded the collection of sphagnum moss from Ireland's bogs, turning it into dressings that saved thousands of lives at the Front.

046 JAMIE DELVES

Jamie's a copywriter who works between the twin capitals. In Edinburgh he works for the lang cat; in London he works for the British Heart Foundation.

'Hans Von Volkmann was a distant relative. My poem imagines him as a champion of Germany's brief colonial project, reflecting at the end of the war.'

047 TONI STUART

Toni Stuart is a South African poet and performer, who uses poetry to excavate the buried and forgotten histories of the country's mixed heritage communities.

The Cape Coloured Corps was formed in segregated South Africa for the war. They fought in East Africa, Egypt, Palestine, turning battles but receiving little recognition.

048 HANNAH RILEY

Hannah is a senior freelance copywriter for brands big, small, established and new. She also writes about mumhood when not running – or running after her toddler.

Allen H Fry, a military photographer, yet son of a Quaker pacifist. Images created as wartime propaganda, designed to foster pride at home and loyalty abroad.

049 PHILIP PARKER

Philip Parker is a writer, editor and researcher. He commenced his career in book publishing, worked in the charitable sector and is now in the corporate.

George Ellison, the last British soldier killed in action during the War, is buried in Belgium opposite John Parr, the first killed. (Goodnight kiss = sniper's final bullet)

050 KATIE-ROSE COMERY

I'm a writer and consultant at The Writer. Before that I was at Sage, writing speeches for the CEO. Once scripted a conversation for a robot.

'My great-grandmother's brother, Stuart Fletcher, spent his two days' leave tracking down his idol – composer Maurice Ravel. Bet his family were miffed he didn't go home.'

051 STEPHEN BARNABY

As a rule, Stephen writes and performs stories of 50 words, so this 100 word challenge has tested his stamina immensely. He is currently lying down.

'As a cricket obsessive, I'd long been aware of the brilliant but vulnerable Charlie Blythe. His life and death ache with pathos, like the war itself.'

052 TOM COLLINS

Tom Collins OBE is an Irish journalist and academic. He is a senior lecturer at the University of Stirling where he teaches Communications, Media and Culture.

Francis Ledwidge wrote one of the most perfect lines in Irish poetry. His poem, Thomas McDonagh, symbolises the spirit of a nation struggling for its freedom.

053 VIVIEN JONES

Vivien is a writer, editor, project leader and Literature Ambassador in the south of Scotland, where she writes poetry, short stories and plays.

Jessie Jane Paterson trained as a nurse in Ayrshire and Glasgow. She served in military 'hospitals' in Salonika – often just tents – and died there of dysentery.

054 JANE BERNEY

A blonde copywriter. Devoted enunciator. Finds gold hiding in jargon. Keeps lofty memory notes. Occupies places quaintly rustic. Senses that uncurtailed, video will extinguish youth's zeal.

When war threatens to take the lives of those that you love, how can you protect them? Throw open the farm gates and send them packing.

055 RICHARD PELLETIER

Child of industrial New England, frequent dreamer. Occasional doer. Restless. Writer for business, picture maker, lover of jazz, coffee, woods, sea, people, trouble. Dark Angels wingman.

Kertesz. Had to be. Fought in the war. Photographed the war. Humble and great. Never quite at home in the world. Romantic. That heart. That eye.

056 WENDY JONES

Wendy is a journalist, broadcaster, writer, teacher and all-round communicator. She toiled at the BBC for many years and (for most of the time) loved it.

'My grandmother Laura Leavesley joined the WAAC as a cook in 1917 and went to France, the year after her brother Arthur died on the Somme.'

057　JOHN BURWELL

John Burwell helps small businesses communicate using media and technology. He prefers black coffee, black shirts, black hearts, and Oxford commas. John doesn't believe in moose.

'I chose a name I recognized but didn't know. He died before his death could have meaning. The street, we remember, but the man, we forget.'

058　JAMIE JAUNCEY

Jamie Jauncey has spent 30 years helping organisations and individuals to find their voices and tell their stories. He is also a blogger, novelist and musician.

'My grandfather, Angus Cunninghame Graham, served as a sub-lieutenant at the Battle of Jutland in 1916. He retired from the Royal Navy, an admiral, in 1951.'

059　HEATHER ATCHISON

A Euro-Yank who loves helping people create a better brand experience through their words: I develop brand language, write, train – and dabble with the odd poem. enoughsaid.co

First black American fighter pilot. Fled Georgia for France. Fought for égalité. Escaped to US during WW2 and ended life as an elevator operator in NYC.

060　PETER NOONE

The 26 Armistice Project is new territory for Peter Noone. He usually works as a freelance writer helping businesses communicate in Plain English. He often succeeds.

Occasionally, ordinary people achieve extraordinary things. William Coltman, the most decorated non-commissioned soldier of the First World War, despite being unarmed, is one of those people.

061　MICHAEL LONGLEY

One of Northern Ireland's foremost contemporary poets, Michael Longley CBE is renowned for the quiet beauty of his compact, meditative lyrics. Recipient of Wilfred Owen Award.

Richard Longley enlisted as a boy soldier. Four years later he had won the Military Cross and become Captain. He never told his son of his heroism.

062　PAUL WHITE

Paul White is a copywriter. He writes poetry and short stories. The shortest story he's ever written (160 words) was published in the UK magazine Flash.

Many of Kenneth White's men at the front were no more than boys a few years older than his pupils at Aranui school in New Zealand.

063　SINÉAD KEEGAN

Sinéad Keegan is a poet, writer, editor and university lecturer currently living in London. Her work appears in print and online. She is co-editor of www.allthesins.co.uk

Countess Constance Markievicz was a leader of the Irish Nationalist movement and a sniper during the 1916 Easter Uprising, where she kissed her gun on surrender.

064　SALLY HARPER

Writes mainly for charities. Guilty ex-history student who didn't go to enough lectures. Now actively seeks out dusty books, decaying objects and stories about dead relatives.

'Alice. My great grandmother. A mum of two with a husband and brother away fighting. But life went on, and so did her to do list.'

065 BEVERLEY MOORE

Beverley is a copywriter specialising in business-to-business and services web content. She also provides business and science writing workshops plus individual writing skills coaching.

'Naval signalman Harry Turner, my great-grandfather, was posted to the Irish coastguard at Malin Head radio station. Did he handle 'live bait squad' SOS messages? Maybe.'

066 MIKE GOGAN

Of Dublin. Its river bridged by Irish writers' names. Born under the shadow, shelter and shenanigans of the tower at Sandycove where James Joyce's Ulysses opens.

'I wrote about my grandfather. I never met him, but his influences as a gentleman merchant and benefactor fleck in the fabric of our family history.'

067 TRACY JO BARNWELL

Tracy Jo Barnwell has published poetry, fiction, and other stuff in books, journals, and elsewhere. In her spare time she plays bluegrass and fights imaginary dragons.

'I stumbled on Frank Baker's journal while researching the Halifax Explosion. I was struck by the fact that he was a writer with an impossible job.'

068 SUE EVANS

Sue Evans is a freelance writer and researcher working in design. She has recently embarked on a two-year undergraduate diploma in Creative Writing at Oxford University.

Tattersall Wilkinson, sage and poet, saw Halley's Comet twice in his lifetime. Imagine his sorrow at the young lives lost, Lancashire lads never to come home.

069 TAMARA O'BRIEN

Tamara O'Brien has spent a life in English language and literature. Was a student and teacher. Now a writer and promoter. Always a reader and lover.

How do you convey true nobility and courage? A German officer's sneering remark propelled the poem, by putting a national heroine in a grubby, human light.

070 JOHN J SILLS

John is, like most writers, addicted to people watching. He particularly enjoys writing about those wonderful moments of humorous human behaviour seen during his weekday commute.

'This piece is inspired by my Grandad, John James Sills. In many ways our lives are very similar, yet at the same time, they're world's apart.'

071 ANDY MILLIGAN

Andy has authored several business books, including Brand It Like Beckham and the award-winning BOLD, as well as the Dark Angels Collective novel, Keeping Mum.

'After her death, my friend discovered his grandmother had a first marriage to Robert Bowman. Intrigued, my friend traced Robert's history to his death near Ypres.'

072 SUSANNAH HART

Susannah Hart lives in London where she works as a brand writer. She also writes poetry and her first collection will be published later this year.

In Lavery's painting of this name neither of the nurses depicted has a recognisable face. Was this just corner-cutting or was there another more significant reason?

073 CAROLINE HOPPER

Caroline's a writer at the agency Quietroom, where she tackles gritty subjects like pensions and healthcare. This 26 project is her grittiest writing subject by far.

Clara went from enemy of the police to police officer herself. She fought for women's rights and then protected women munitions workers' welfare in Pembrey, Wales.

074 RAPH ADAS

Raphelita left rural Jamaica for the city with her little bag. Did all kinds of work. At 65 writes poems, enjoys gardening and her grandson. Old-but-not-cold. Related to Marc Boothe who heads up B3 Media - a creative arts network. He also produces Talentlab – an innovative, creative arts lab which supports BAME emerging artists, filmmakers and digital storytellers.

Inspired by Mary Seacole, Jamaican nurses went to Europe to help the wounded and dying, the men of BWIR fighting for a country they didn't know.

075 FRANCESCA BAKER

Curious and creative, Francesca Baker loves to explore the world, and write about it. She writes personally and professionally, and, sometimes, both. Find her online @andsoshethinks.

'Francis Henry Dutton was my great-great-uncle on my father's mother's side. Or would have been, if he hadn't been killed in battle aged 18.'

076 SAM KNOWLES

I'm Sam, a storyteller for business. My purpose is to help companies sound human. Data anchors my stories, and I'm the author of Narrative by Numbers.

Lewes Remembers 2017 saw 236 locals walk with torches, from homes of Lewes WWI fallen to the War Memorial. George Crock's story was the most extraordinary.

077 ROWENA ROBERTS

Rowena Roberts, copywriter, works under the name Words Inspire, in honour of all emotions stirred, ideas influenced and actions motivated by simple scribbles across human history.

'Untold stories shuddered between simple lines of love, domesticity and minor military irritations in George Davison's letters to his wife. I told them. Lest we forget.'

078 STEPHEN POTTS

Stephen Potts writes screenplays and children's adventure fiction, specialising in historically set stories. By day he is a psychiatrist in Edinburgh's transplant unit. www.stephenpotts.net

'Cavalryman at the start, machine-gunner by the end, my grandfather David McNally said nothing of his service. I chose to tell his story for him.'

079 JEROME CAIN

Jerome is a thirty something, Hertfordshire born, Lambeth living, agency working, spare time writing, movie enthusiast. He's inspired by people, and people that write people well.

Henry Johnson, a snapshot of war through the eyes of a minority. A tale of division, unexpected inclusion, and final division. Determination, mortality, but ultimately, legacy.

080 BRIDGET WATERS

Bridget is a writer and fundraising consultant based in Liverpool. She helps charities to find funding, tell compelling stories, and win support from trusts and foundations.

Captain Noel Godfrey Chavasse, VC & Bar, MC was a British medical doctor and the only man to receive two Victoria Crosses during the Great War.

081 ELISE VALMORBIDA

Elise Valmorbida is an Italian-Australian writer. Her latest novel, The Madonna of the Mountains, is published by Faber & Faber and internationally in several languages. www.elisevalmorbida.com

'My Italian grandfathers defended their mountains against Austrian invasion: The War in Snow and Ice. Stories, histories, battles, have many sides, but who tells what tales?'

082 DAVID BATY

David Baty has a background in research, management consulting, and talent development. Beyond the commercial world, his writing interests are in travel stories, and historical fiction.

Remembering the tunnellers who fought a hidden war underneath the battlefields. Inspired by William Hackett VC who died, refusing rescue, to look after an injured comrade.

083 JAN DEKKER

Jan helps banks, consultants, telecoms titans and more to find their voice, tell their stories and share their thoughts. All without leveraging synergies or aligning competencies.

Hermann Steven survived to tell his story to his nephew, Josef Bröker. Jan first heard it from Josef's daughter Katja, and then from Josef himself.

084 MICHELLE NICOL

Copywriter, brand storyteller and writer of words that attract attention. A former BBC journalist, when she's not scribbling in notebooks, Michelle also enjoys running and triathlon.

'Photograph of my Nana and her sisters taken in 1918 to mark the safe return home of their father John Robert Anderson from World War One.'

085 HENRIETTA McKERVEY

Dublin-based design & advertising copywriter turned fiction writer. My new novel Violet Hill (publ. June by Hachette) features two highly unusual detectives, separated by a century.

By 1918, Sir Arthur Conan Doyle had lost his first wife, brother, brothers-in-law, nephews, and son Kingsley. He was determined to contact Kingsley again. But how?

086 MARTIN LEE

By day, Martin co-runs an agency called Acacia Avenue. By night, he dreams. And in the times between, he writes for a life, not a living.

A girl survives the war but loses four brothers, eventually becoming the loving grandmother of a friend who posts her story on Facebook on Armistice Day.

087 SOPHIE GORDON

By day, Sophie is an in-house copywriter for the NSPCC. She also helps to edit 26's newsletter and recently launched Beings magazine.

Monet remained in Giverny throughout the war, painting and contributing to charitable efforts. In 1918 he gifted 12 paintings to France, in honour of the armistice.

088 MONIKA LEHNER

I've lived in Austria, Japan, the UK and Germany. Writing helps me understand the world. I'm grateful that it has, over time, also become my profession.

'My grandmother, aged nine, survived the war's biggest killer – Spanish flu – then became a serial refugee. Proof that ideas of national identity verge on the fictional.'

089 DAVID & JORDAN BICKERTON

Thoughtful communicator. Hybrid model with corporate, consulting and academic background. Current Director of Communications at BP where he puts words in others' mouths. Father of two, one of whom is Jordan.

Castrol founder, Lord Mayor of London and philanthropist, Charles Cheers Wakefield threw open the doors of Mansion House to everyone from wounded soldiers to orphaned children.

090 ROB BRIGGS

Rob is deeply passionate about business communications, people and how companies can best manage their reputations. He lives with a demanding dog and a loving wife.

'Albert Ball VC went to my school… but researching this WWI flying ace drew me to a new perspective, looking at Ball from the enemy's viewpoint.'

091 IRENE LOFTHOUSE

Writer. Creative catalyst. Gardener. Storyteller. Dog trainer. Actor. Decorator. Playwright. Facilitator. Writer in Residence. Irene wears as many hats as costumes depending on the day/project.

'Grandad was a bastard, went to war, married a woman a foot taller, couldn't work, fathered four children, died. That I know. The rest's a mystery.'

092 ROGER N MORRIS

Roger Morris writes fiction as R. N. Morris. His books include a series of detective novels set in London before and during the First World War.

White feathers as a symbol of cowardice were given to 'shirkers' – young men who had not enlisted. After receiving one such feather, Robert Grieves killed himself.

093 JOHN ALLERT

John Allert is Chief Marketing Officer of McLaren Technology Group, the iconic Formula1 racing team. An Aussie based in UK, he writes and lectures on branding.

'Great-grand-uncle Les was a pacifist. Signed up so brother Mervyn would not be alone. His job – corpse collection – at Gallipoli, the Somme. "Les never came back."'

094 SUZIE INMAN

Suzie lives and writes in deepest Cornwall where she crafts creative copy for web and print as mightier. co.uk And when she can she's a fiction superhero…

One the tragedies of the war was the lives not taken, the opportunities lost thanks to the upheaval – dreams and ambitions put on hold.

095 DAVID MATHEWS

A psychologist, David researched and wrote about work. Now he writes stories, some about his native Wales, but all about our daft and heroic human condition.

The National Library of Wales holds 531 glass negatives, images by HW Lloyd of Bala, pharmacist. Among them, portraits of prisoners at Frongoch PoW Camp.

096 JONATHAN BARNES

Jonathan writes stories of gothic transformation - in the novels The Somnambulist, The Domino Men and Cannonbridge and in adaptations of Dracula, Frankenstein and The Invisible Man.

Tolkien denied parallels between Middle Earth and our world. The exception? The Dead Marshes which 'owe something to Northern France after the Battle of the Somme.'

097 GITA RALLEIGH

Gita Ralleigh is a medical consultant and writer. Her work has appeared in Wasafiri, Bellevue Literary Review and in anthologies by Freight and The Emma Press.

Manta Singh died a hero. Shot while rescuing an officer at Neuve Chapelle, his name is carved on a memorial stone high on the South Downs.

098 JOAN LENNON

Joan Lennon is a Canadian Scot, living and writing in the Kingdom of Fife, with a fine view of rooftops, trees, Dundee and the silvery Tay.

'My grandfather served with the Canadian Army Medical Corps before going to China as a medical missionary, where he died, leaving so many questions without answers…'

099 SUE BURGE

Sue Burge is a chocoholic poet and freelance creative writing/film studies tutor based North Norfolk. She loves walking, swimming and the cinema. More at www.sueburge.uk

'Augustin's death 15 minutes before the war officially ended haunted me, as did the intentionally wrong date on his memorial, the day before he actually died.'

100 FAYE SHARPE

Faye is retired. That is to say, she has ceased doing and is now being. She once did (and was) many things. Now she's a writer.

'I was once an archaeologist, an osteologist to be precise. I know what it is to stare into empty orbits and wonder, "Whose face was this?"'

HOW TO WRITE A CENTENA

John Simmons & Ed Prichard

How to write a centena

The centena is a new poetic form invented for
the centenary partnership 100 Days/Armistice
project between Imperial War Museums and the
writers' group 26 (www.26.org.uk). We asked
John Simmons, founder director of 26 and
creator of the centena form, and Ed Prichard,
one of the project's writers and editors, to tell
us more about it – with the hope that others in
our community might try it. They conducted the
following conversation.

John to Ed
Ed, it's surprising how quickly the idea of
writing centenas for the project between 26 and
IWM became established. Can you remember
how you first heard of the idea? What was your
reaction?

Ed to John
I was intrigued by it and excited by the idea of
commemorating a centenary with a new form
that reflects the passing years. I love the way a
restriction – whether it's number of words or
starting every sentence with the same letter for
example – really focuses your writing. The three
repeated words at the start and end give the
form a satisfying symmetry too – another chance
to test your creativity. It gives you a different way
in – you almost have to start at the end.

John to Ed

I've long believed in the liberating power of constraints, and have even written books on it. Counter-intuitive as it sounds, it's a creative release because your mind, having been hemmed in, finds a way to break out. So when I came to think about the brief, I was looking for a creative constraint that would be appropriate for a centenary. 100 words was obvious but I thought it also needed a structural device to encourage a complete piece – so beginning and ending with the same three words came into my head.

In the case of my own centena, the words 'He looked up' were my starting point, as I thought about my grandfather (killed by bullets fired from a German plane in 1917). It just seemed right, and would work as an ending too. I then had 94 words to get from the beginning of the story to its ending.

Did you have a similar process? Did the first three words come first? I'm sure different writers will approach it in different ways.

Ed to John

Often it's a phrase that sticks in your head that kicks off the writing. I wanted to write in the first person and I had an idea about my great grandmother, Catherine, looking back from thirty years after the war ended through a fog of dementia. She lost two sons and the third was wounded and died the year before she did in 1952. As a widow, the consequences for her family weren't great – my great aunt and grandmother were sent into service, which was pretty grim.

Catherine lived in a mining village called Abertridwr in the valleys, so I had the idea that she was thinking about the two places. Her eldest son, Benjamin John, died at Gallipoli in the Dardanelles, a long way from home, which gave me another contrast to play with.

I let it all sit for a while and the first words came from a bit of word play on the Dardanelles. If you repeat it over and over, it starts to lose meaning and, to me, it sounds a bit like a train. Then something clicked – in her confusion, she's going to catch a train to bring him home. So my opening and closing three words are: 'Dardanelles-denelles-denelles he never...' Because of the dementia aspect, I wanted the end to trail off as her mind wanders.

I think the three words are a good place to start – especially as you want to start strongly to grab the reader's attention and aim to end on the same note. The challenge is then to tell the story with so few words, so every word has to count. How did you go about editing your centena?

John to Ed
Well, of course, to edit you need to have written something. My advice is to start writing without worrying about the word count for the first draft. You can, for example, start with a piece of automatic writing in which you just put words down, almost in a stream of consciousness way, with no editing while you write. If you write non-stop for five minutes you will almost certainly have more than 100 words – which gives you something to work with.

Or you might, as I did, have a few phrases that pop into your head. In my case it was 'he was listening to the birds' and 'the last thing he was thinking of'. These came from imagining my grandfather writing a letter home just before he was killed. I have some of his letters to my Nan so I know this was something he did. I imagined him engrossed in distractions such as birds singing and thoughts of home – so engrossed that he didn't see the German plane overhead. All I knew of my grandad's death was that he was strafed by bullets from a plane. It was still such an unusual event that he might not have considered a plane a threat.

So I was putting together the pieces of the story. Now I needed to write a draft. I did this while flying from Singapore to New Zealand – I find travelling conducive to writing. My first draft was much more than 100 words but that was OK – editing is an essential part of writing and now I had something to edit.

At this point other aspects of writing kick in – the shape of the poem on the page, decisions about lines and rhymes (yes or no), the rhythm of the words. Because I imagined the words as coming from my grandmother's mouth I wanted them to sound spoken – but also to have an incantatory effect, as if spoken to herself, to give herself some comfort. At this point I decided to put most of the verbs into the present tense, with the –ing ending of verbs to make it sound more immediate, in the moment. It also meant that these were, if not rhymes, then half-rhymes which would give a fractured intensity to the words. Then to emphasise some of these by placing them as single words on a line.

All of this meant that the centena was taking shape. It was now close to its intended number of words. The final stages of drafting (after the plane trip was done) whittled down from 108 to 100 words, and was the most time-consuming stage. To cut out words but leave everything essential. But in many ways the most enjoyable because by then you know you have something. You just need to work at getting the final form, like one of those puzzles where you push squares around until everything fits in the right places.

Then you live with it for a while – days or weeks – until you're convinced it can be shown more widely: first to my wife and daughter, then to my editor Richard. They were positive, indicating that I had made an emotional connection. A relief. All writers allow their work out into the world with some trepidation. You never quite get over that, do you? There's always a bit of bravery needed.

Ed to John
You're right, there's always a moment when you know it's ready but it's still nerve-wracking letting it out there. I shared an earlier draft at a writing workshop, which I found helpful – the combination of reading it out loud and hearing other people's reactions was good. Fortunately, the feedback was positive. Once it's out there, it takes on another life as people read and share it.

I've been through a similar journey to you while writing mine, trying to put myself inside my great grandmother's head. The final poem came out as a stream of consciousness that meanders over the page, reflecting her confused state of mind. Once I realised that was how it would look on paper, it made writing the rest a bit easier.

I found researching the background helped me a lot too – finding information online about the world in 1918 and how people lived was really useful. Then cross-referencing it back to my family story made it feel more real. I used an ancestry website to research the family tree and found lots of documents on there that were fascinating. For example, my great uncle Gwilym's service records show when he was wounded in Gallipoli and then again in Flanders, where he was in hospital and all sorts of details.

I also searched in the newspaper archives online. It's easy to fall down the rabbit hole and get sidetracked (which was brilliant for getting a feel of the world at that time). But I did find a newspaper article that mentioned my great grandmother and her sons, which added flesh to some of things I'd found elsewhere.

Once you get going, it's amazing what you find in the strangest places. I searched for my great grandmother's house in Abertridwr and found it on a property site. There were photos and a floor plan; somehow two adults and 10 children, from the age of 3 up to 25, all rubbed along together in a tiny three-bedroom cottage. It doesn't appear in the poem, but it gave me context.

The archive recommended by IWM was very helpful too. They couldn't give me specific information about Catherine or the family, but the background was very useful. They also gave me some clues about where else to look. It seems there are lots of local projects all over the country that have built websites and collections from people's personal submissions about their families.

It's easy to be overwhelmed by the sheer amount of information, websites and archives out there. So if you can start with general searches and then get more specific, that's a good way in. Local archives are a good place to start or even your local library. One thing I found useful was to keep careful notes on where I found things – I lost the sources of a couple of things as I got a bit overexcited when I found them!

John to Ed
The wonderful thing about this kind of research is that you never know where it will lead you. There will be surprises – welcome them. The other resources we have are inside our heads in the form of imagination and memory, those close cousins. As well as your own memory, tap into the memories of friends and family members – but know that, in the end, it's your perspective that counts. Be brave – an essential quality for a writer – and trust that if the subject moves you, it will also move the reader.

WAR CHILD

War Child is striving for a world with no child's life torn apart by war.

We protect, educate and stand up for the rights of children caught up in conflict. Our aim is to reach them as early as possible when conflict breaks out, and stay to support them through their recovery, helping to keep them safe, give them an education, and equip them with skills for the future.

We're still the only charity dedicated to protecting and speaking up for children affected by war, because we believe that War and Child are two words that should never go together.

You can find out more and support War Child at: www.warchild.org.uk

26 Characters Ltd™ is a diverse group of people who share a love of words, and believe their potential is hugely underestimated. Many of us work with words for a living, as writers, language specialists, editors, designers or publishers, but anyone who cares about words is welcome to join 26. Together, we hope to raise the profile and value of words not only in business, but also in everyday life.

Individuals, businesses, charities and government bodies all have compelling stories to tell – and we hope to show them how experienced and imaginative writers can find new and credible ways to engage their audiences. But we also want to open hearts and minds to the wonderful diversity of writing, to savour and enjoy words in all their many guises… and to have some fun.

We chose the name 26 because there are 26 letters in the alphabet – the DNA of language. We're a not-for-profit organisation.

If you would like to find out more and be part of 26, visit: 26.org.uk

G . F
SMITH

Text pages printed on Munken Design
Endpapers printed on Colorplan Vermillion Red